AS/A-LEVEL YEARS 1 AN[D]

STUDENT GUIDE

OCR

Physics A and B

Practical assessment

Carol Davenport and Graham George

Series editor: Graham George

HODDER
EDUCATION
AN HACHETTE UK COMPANY

Hodder Education, an Hachette UK company, Blenheim Court, George Street, Banbury, Oxfordshire OX16 5BH

Orders

Bookpoint Ltd, 130 Park Drive, Milton Park, Abingdon, Oxfordshire OX14 4SE

tel: 01235 827827

fax: 01235 400401

e-mail: education@bookpoint.co.uk

Lines are open 9.00 a.m.–5.00 p.m., Monday to Saturday, with a 24-hour message answering service. You can also order through the Hodder Education website: www.hoddereducation.co.uk

© Carol Davenport and Graham George 2016

ISBN 978-1-4718-8517-4

First printed 2017

Impression number 5 4 3 2 1

Year 2020 2019 2018 2017

This guide has been written specifically to support students preparing for the OCR A-level Physics examinations. The content has been neither approved nor endorsed by OCR and remains the sole responsibility of the authors.

Cover photo: Peter Hermes Furian/Fotolia; page 69 GIPhotostock/SPL

Typeset by Integra Software Services Pvt. Ltd, Pondicherry, India

Printed in Italy

Hachette UK's policy is to use papers that are natural, renewable and recyclable products and made from wood grown in sustainable forests. The logging and manufacturing processes are expected to conform to the environmental regulations of the country of origin.

Contents

Content Guidance

Questions & Answers

■ About this book

This guide covers the practical assessment for OCR specifications A and B for AS and A-level physics. It offers advice for the effective development of practical skills. Its aim is to help you understand and put into practice the physics — it is not intended as a replacement for carrying out practical work. The guide has four sections:

- The **Maths and Units** section incorporates the mathematical skills that you need for the AS and A-level examination, together with a reminder of the importance of units. For A-level you need more advanced mathematical skills, which are highlighted in **bold**. This section provides the basis of all calculations that you will be required to undertake and that is why it is the first section in the book. Without these mathematical skills, you will not be able to analyse your data and subsequently draw conclusions about your experiment. You are advised to work through this section to remind yourself of the essential mathematics and put your knowledge to the test by attempting the questions as you go along. You may also find it useful to refer back to this section when you are trying questions later in the book.

- The **Practical Skills** section identifies the essential skills needed for successful practical work, based on the practical criteria set out in the specification. It will help you become a confident practical physicist, able to use a variety of apparatus and techniques to collect data, which can then be analysed and used to draw valid conclusions.

- The **Practical Activity Groups** (PAGs) section reflects the OCR requirement that you should acquire competence and confidence in a variety of practical, mathematical and problem-solving skills and in handling apparatus competently and safely. Each of the PAGs is discussed in detail, focusing on one practical identified in the specification, with worked examples based on experimental data. You may have also used other practical activities linked to each PAG, and other possible activities will be highlighted for each PAG. For the AS examination, you need only be familiar with PAGs 1–6.

- The **Questions & Answers** section pulls together the other three sections through a range of practice questions based on the type of question that will be asked in examination papers to test practical knowledge, particularly in Paper 3. It does *not* in itself replicate a complete examination paper, as it contains only questions that test practical skills. Answers are provided, and common errors made by students are also highlighted so that you, hopefully, do not make the same mistakes.

If you are reading this, you are clearly determined to do well in your examinations! If you try all the knowledge check questions, the worked examples and the questions at the end *before* looking at the answers, you will begin to think for yourself and develop the necessary techniques for answering examination questions. As the answers to the worked examples are an integral part of the learning process, they appear immediately after the questions. You are recommended to cover up the answers before attempting the question — this will improve your ability to answer similar questions in future. If you 'cheat' by looking up the answers first, you are only cheating yourself.

Thus prepared, you will be able to approach the examination with confidence. Good luck, and remember that physics is fun!

Content Guidance

■ Maths and units

Throughout your AS or A-level course, you will make use of a range of mathematical knowledge and techniques. Some of these, such as basic algebra, will be used regularly in many different topics. Others, such as logarithms, will only be needed in a few topics. In this section, we shall cover the range of mathematical skills required during your course, with a particular focus on how they are used in practical work. Those statements in **bold** will be assessed in the full A-level course only.

Arithmetic and units

Correctly interpreting numerical information is an important first step in many practical calculations in physics.

Throughout your studies you will need to:

- recognise and make use of appropriate units in calculations
- recognise and use expressions in decimal and standard form
- use ratios, fractions and percentages
- estimate results
- use calculators to find and use power functions, **exponential** and **logarithmic functions**
- use calculators to handle $\sin x$, $\cos x$ and $\tan x$ when x is expressed in degrees or radians

Exam tip

Always look carefully at the units in any numerical data. It is often helpful to convert units into standard units such as metres (m), rather than leave them as millimetres (mm).

Physical measurements are expressed in standard (SI) units. These have been agreed internationally so that the same value and unit for each is used in different countries. Table 1 shows some examples of SI units.

Table 1 SI units

Quantity	Unit	Symbol
Length	metre	m
Mass	kilogram	kg
Time	second	s
Electric current	ampere	A
Temperature	kelvin	K
Amount of substance	mole	mol

Knowledge check 1

Give the following units in terms of base SI units:
a joule, J
b coulomb, C
c ohm, Ω
d watt, W

These base SI units are combined to give units for other quantities. The units of many commonly used quantities are given their own names. For example, force is measured in newtons (N), but this can be expressed as $\text{kg}\,\text{m}\,\text{s}^{-2}$; pressure is measured in pascals (Pa), which is the same as $\text{kg}\,\text{m}^{-1}\,\text{s}^{-2}$.

Content Guidance

For very small or very large measurements, prefixes are used. Table 2 gives some of the common prefixes used in physics.

Table 2 Common prefixes used in physics

Name and symbol	Factor of 10	Name and symbol	Factor of 10
centi, c	10^{-2}		
milli, m	10^{-3}	kilo, k	10^{3}
micro, μ	10^{-6}	mega, M	10^{6}
nano, n	10^{-9}	giga, G	10^{9}
pico, p	10^{-12}	tera, T	10^{12}
femto, f	10^{-15}		

Knowledge check 2

A student is investigating the density of a length of wooden dowelling. She measures the diameter of the wood to be 12.7 mm and the length of the dowelling as 80.0 cm. She calculates that the area of cross-section of the dowelling is 127 mm^2 and that its volume is 102 cm^3. Convert these four measurements into m, m^2 and m^3, expressing your answers in standard form if appropriate.

Worked example

(A-level only) A student is measuring the gravitational attraction between two masses, M and m. Estimate what happens to the gravitational force between the masses when the distance separating them is halved.

Answer

For the original force

$$F_1 = \frac{GMm}{r^2}$$

When the distance is halved

$$F_2 = \frac{GMm}{\left(\frac{r}{2}\right)^2} = \frac{GMm}{\frac{r^2}{4}} = \frac{4GMm}{r^2}$$

But $\frac{GMm}{r^2} = F_1$ so $F_2 = 4F_1$.

Sometimes, when solving real-world problems in physics, you will not have all the information that you need. It is helpful to be able to make a reasonable estimate for the answer to the problem. This can be done using order-of-magnitude figures for the variables in the problem. The physicist Enrico Fermi was able to calculate the approximate strength of the first nuclear bomb detonated in 1945. Watching the fireball of the explosion from 16 km away, Fermi dropped some small pieces of paper. He watched how they fell before, during and after the explosion. He estimated that the strength of the bomb was approximately 10 kilotons. The actual value was 20 kilotons.

Knowledge check 3

The light from a laser has a wavelength of 643 nm and a diffraction grating has a distance between slits of 3.3 μm. Express these values in m using standard form.

Exam tip

Always check whether the values you are given in an exam question have a prefix. Convert these into standard form before you attempt to answer the question.

Exam tip

Multiple-choice questions will often require you to make use of ratios to decide how changing one of the variables in an equation will affect another variable.

Knowledge check 4

The refractive index of olive oil is 1.47 and the refractive index of water is 1.33. Calculate the ratio speed of light in water (c_w) : speed of light in olive oil (c_o).

Worked example

A drop of vegetable oil, 0.5 mm in diameter, is dropped onto the surface of a tray of water. The oil spreads out across the water in a circular shaped layer with a diameter of 250 mm. Assuming that the layer is one molecule thick, estimate the size of a vegetable oil molecule.

Answer

The volume of the drop of vegetable oil remains the same whether it is as a drop or as the circular layer.

For the drop volume — approximate the drop to a cube:

$$\text{volume} = (0.5 \times 10^{-3}\,\text{m})^3 \approx 1 \times 10^{-10}\,\text{m}^3$$

For the layer volume — approximate the layer of oil on water to a square:

$$\text{volume} = (0.25\,\text{m})^2 \times \text{thickness} \approx (1 \times 10^{-1})\,\text{m}^2 \times d$$

where d is the thickness of one molecule.

Equating the two volumes gives:

$$1 \times 10^{-10}\,\text{m}^3 = 1 \times 10^{-1} \times d$$

So $d \approx 1 \times 10^{-9}\,\text{m}$.

This is an estimate of the largest size that a molecule may be, because the film may be more than one molecule thick.

At A-level, exponentials and logarithms are mainly found in the topics of capacitance and radioactivity. Exponential growth occurs when the variable you are measuring increases by the same proportion in each equal interval of time. Exponential decay occurs when the measured variable decreases by the same proportion in each equal interval of time.

Worked example

(A-level only) The potential difference (p.d.) V (in V) across a capacitor of capacitance C (in F) that is discharging through a resistor of resistance R (in Ω) decreases exponentially with time t (in s) according to the equation

$$V = V_0 e^{-t/RC}$$

where V_0 is the initial p.d. at t_0.

A student is using data logging equipment to investigate the discharge of a capacitor. The capacitor has a labelled capacitance of 220 μF and is charged to 8.0 V. The capacitor is discharged through a 470 kΩ resistor. Calculate the p.d. across the capacitor after 60 s.

→

Knowledge check 5

a If X is 120, what is 40% of X?
b If 20% of X is 60, what is X?
c If 25% of X is 2.0×10^3, what is X?

Knowledge check 6

A student is determining the refractive index of a transparent block. Using a protractor, the student measures the angle of incidence as 35.5° and the angle of refraction as 26.0°. Calculate the refractive index of the block.

Knowledge check 7

What are the values of $\sin\theta$, $\cos\theta$ and $\tan\theta$ for the following angles?
a $\theta = 0°$; b $\theta = 45°$;
c $\theta = \pi$ rad; d $\theta = \pi/2$ rad

Exam tip

If a question involves angles in radians, make sure that you use your calculator in the radian or rad mode for your calculations.

Answer

Using $V = V_0 e^{-t/RC}$ where $V_0 = 8.0\,\text{V}$ gives:

$$V = 8.0\,\text{V} \times e^{-\left(\frac{60\,\text{s}}{470 \times 10^3\,\Omega \times 220 \times 10^{-6}\,\text{F}}\right)} = 8.0\,\text{V} \times e^{-0.580}$$

$$V = 8.0\,\text{V} \times 0.560 = 4.5\,\text{V}$$

Handling data

During most practical work you will collect data of some form. You will need to process the data in a suitable way to allow you to draw conclusions about the experiment.

Throughout your studies you will need to:

- use an appropriate number of significant figures (s.f.)
- find arithmetic means
- understand simple probability
- make order-of-magnitude calculations
- identify uncertainties in measurements and use simple techniques to determine uncertainty when data are combined by addition, subtraction, multiplication, division and raising to powers

Significant figures are the figures in a number that are meaningful or useful. When doing a practical, the number of significant figures recorded in your data will depend on the precision of the equipment you are using. You can find more detail about precision and uncertainties on pages 22–23.

Using experimental data to calculate other variables with your calculator will often result in an answer with a lot of decimal places. When writing out the answers, round up or down to give the answer to the same number of significant figures as the original data.

A student is measuring the Young modulus of a copper wire. The following measurements of the diameter of the wire are taken at five different places along the wire using a micrometer:

0.37 mm	0.38 mm	0.36 mm	0.38 mm	0.37 mm

Calculate:

a the mean diameter of the wire

b the cross-sectional area of the wire

Give your answers to an appropriate number of significant figures.

$\rightarrow$

Exam tip

Always check your answer to see if it is sensible and of the right magnitude. For example, if the value for the voltage after 60 s is larger than the initial value of 8.0 V, you have probably not used the minus sign in the exponential.

Knowledge check 8

Do the following calculations, giving your answers in standard form to the appropriate number of significant figures.

a $\frac{4}{3}\pi(6.37 \times 10^6)^3$

b $430\,\text{THz} \times 700\,\text{nm}$

c $(0.50 \times 6.0) + (\frac{1}{2} \times 9.8 \times (6.0)^2)$

Exam tip

How many significant figures? When carrying out a calculation using measured data with different numbers of significant figures, your result should contain the same number of significant figures as the measurement with the *smallest* number of significant figures (unless a detailed analysis of the uncertainties suggests otherwise).

Answer

a $\text{mean diameter} = \dfrac{(0.37 + 0.38 + 0.36 + 0.38 + 0.37)\,\text{mm}}{5}$

    $\text{mean diameter} = 0.372\,\text{mm} = 3.72 \times 10^{-4}\,\text{m}$

However, while our calculator gives us 3 s.f., our data have only 2 s.f., so the answer should be given as:

    $\text{mean diameter} = 3.7 \times 10^{-4}\,\text{m}$

b $\text{cross-sectional area} = \pi r^2 = \pi(\tfrac{1}{2} \times 3.72 \times 10^{-4}\,\text{m})^2 = 1.08687 \times 10^{-7}\,\text{m}^2$

Again, rounding down to 2 s.f., the answer should be:

    $\text{cross-sectional area} = 1.1 \times 10^{-7}\,\text{m}^2$

Worked example

A student measures the potential difference across a resistor that is being used as part of a potential divider circuit. The potential difference is measured as 8.0 V. The current in the resistor is 2.96 mA. What is the resistance of the resistor?

Answer

$$R = \frac{V}{I} = \frac{8.0\,\text{V}}{2.96 \times 10^{-3}\,\text{A}} = 2702.7\,\Omega$$

The data in the question are given to 2 s.f. and 3 s.f. The answer should therefore be given to just 2 s.f. However, that would be $2700\,\Omega$, which could be taken to mean 2, 3 or 4 s.f. In this case, it is more useful to give the resistance as $2.7\,\text{k}\Omega$.

Probability is a measure of the likelihood of an event occurring. In physics, you will mainly meet probability in the topic of radioactive decay. The probability of a nucleus decaying in a unit time is constant, known as the decay constant, λ. This gives us the equation for the *rate* of decay (or activity A) as $\dfrac{\text{d}N}{\text{d}t} = -\lambda N$, the minus sign indicating that the activity *decreases* with time.

Algebra

Algebraic equations are used to clearly express the relationship between variables in a physical situation. To solve many problems in A-level physics, you will need to be able to manipulate equations.

Throughout your studies you will need to:

- understand and use the symbols $=, <, \ll, \gg, >, \propto, \approx, \Delta$
- change the subject of an equation, including non-linear equations
- substitute numerical values into algebraic equations using appropriate units for physical quantities
- solve algebraic equations, including quadratic equations
- **use logarithms in relation to quantities that range over several orders of magnitude**

Symbols are a useful form of shorthand in physics. You will be familiar with many of these symbols from earlier in your school career. Some are shown in Table 3.

Table 3 Common symbols

Symbol	Meaning
<<	much less than
>>	much greater than
∝	proportional to
≈	approximately equal to
Δ	change in

Exam tip

You are less likely to make a mistake in calculations if you rearrange the appropriate equations *before* you put the numbers in.

Worked example

(**A-level only**) A student is measuring the specific heat capacity of a block of aluminium. He uses a small heater to heat the block and a thermometer inserted into the block to measure the temperature rise. He obtains the following values:

- Mass of block   0.996 kg
- Energy supplied 2.6×10^4 J
- Initial temperature   18°C
- Final temperature   48°C

Calculate the value of specific heat capacity for the block of aluminium.

Answer

energy supplied = mass × specific heat capacity × temperature change

$$E = mc\Delta\theta$$

First divide both sides by $m\Delta\theta$ to get:

$$\frac{E}{m\Delta\theta} = \frac{mc\Delta\theta}{m\Delta\theta}$$

Cancelling $m\Delta\theta$ from the right-hand side of the equation we get:

$$\frac{E}{m\Delta\theta} = c$$

We can now substitute the values from the experiment into the equation:

$$c = \frac{2.6 \times 10^4\,\text{J}}{0.966\,\text{kg} \times 30\,\text{K}} = 897.17\,\text{J}\,\text{kg}^{-1}\,\text{K}^{-1}$$

The smallest number of significant figures in the data recorded by the student is two. The answer should therefore be given to 2 s.f.:

$$c = 9.0 \times 10^2\,\text{J}\,\text{kg}^{-1}\,\text{K}^{-1}$$

Knowledge check 11

Write the following statements as equations using the appropriate mathematical symbols:

a The work done in an electrical circuit is equal to the potential difference multiplied by the charge.

b The extension of a spring is directly proportional to the applied force on the spring.

c **Magnetic flux is equal to the magnetic flux density multiplied by the area normal to the magnetic field.**

Knowledge check 12

Rearrange the following equations so that the quantity shown in square brackets after each equation is the subject of the rearranged equation.

a $\rho = \dfrac{m}{V}$ [V]

b $p = mv$ [m]

c $V_{\text{out}} = V_{\text{in}} \times \dfrac{R_2}{R_1 + R_2}$ [R_2]

d $v^2 = u^2 + 2as$ [a]

e $n\lambda = d\sin\theta$ [θ]

f $F = m\omega^2 r$ [ω]

Exam tip

Remember that a temperature *difference* in °C is the same as a temperature *difference* in K. For example, here we have $(48 - 18)°C \equiv 30\,\text{K}$.

a Use the equation

moment = Fd

to calculate the moment when $F = 225\,N$ and $d = 7.0\,cm$.

b Use the equation

$$\varepsilon = \frac{x}{L}$$

to calculate L when $\varepsilon = 0.1$ and $x = 10\,cm$.

c (A-level only) Use the equation

$x = A \cos \omega t$

to calculate x when $A = 0.040\,m$, $\omega = \pi/3\,rad\,s^{-1}$ and $t = 11\,s$.

Quadratic equations contain squared terms. The most common quadratic equation that you will meet in AS or A-level physics is the equation of motion:

$$s = ut + \frac{1}{2}at^2$$

Logarithmic scales are used to express data that have a range of several orders of magnitude. Sound is one common phenomenon that is measured using a logarithmic scale. Sound intensity is measured in Wm^{-2}. A typical person can hear very quiet (low-intensity) sounds and extremely loud (high-intensity) sounds. To make a noise *sound* twice as loud, the intensity has to be approximately 10× greater. It would be very difficult to use a linear scale to represent this. A special logarithmic scale, known as the decibel (dB) scale, is used. On this scale, a doubling of intensity is given by an increase of 10 dB (see Table 4).

Table 4 Examples of sound on the decibel scale

Sound	Intensity/Wm^{-2}	Intensity/dB
Whisper	1×10^{-10}	20
Bird call	1×10^{-8}	40
Normal speech	1×10^{-6}	60
Traffic noise	1×10^{-5}	70
Pop/rock concert	1×10^{-1}	110
Pain threshold	1×10^{1}	130

Quantity algebra

Throughout this student guide use has been made of **quantity algebra**. This means giving *every* quantity in an equation its appropriate unit, for example:

$$\rho = \frac{6.95\,\Omega \times 7.79 \times 10^{-8}\,m^2}{0.500\,m} = 1.08 \times 10^{-6}\,\Omega\,m$$

Using quantity algebra gives a useful check for units and can often prevent silly mistakes.

Graphs

It has been said that a picture is worth a thousand words. This is definitely true in physics, where graphs are used to display data, to investigate relationships between variables and to calculate the magnitude of variables. Throughout your studies you will need to:

- translate information between graphical, numerical and algebraic forms
- plot two variables from experimental or other data

A ball is dropped from a height of 1.5 m. How long does it take the ball to reach the ground?

(A-level only) Suggest another physical phenomenon that is measured using a logarithmic scale.

Get into the habit of using quantity algebra so that you can check whether your units are correct or not.

- understand that $y = mx + c$ represents a linear relationship
- determine the slope and intercept of a linear graph
- calculate rate of change from a graph showing a linear relationship
- draw and use the slope of a tangent to a curve as a measure of rate of change
- distinguish between instantaneous rate of change and average rate of change
- understand the possible physical significance of the area between a curve and the x-axis and be able to calculate it or estimate it by graphical methods as appropriate
- apply the concepts underlying calculus to solve equations involving rates of change using a graphical method or spreadsheet modelling
- **interpret logarithmic plots**
- **use logarithmic plots to test exponential and power-law variations**
- sketch physical relationships that are modelled by
  - $y = k/x$
  - $y = kx^2$
  - $y = kx$
  - $y = \sin x$
  - $y = \cos x$
  - $y = e^{\pm x}$
  - $y = \sin^2 x$
  - $y = \cos^2 x$

In general, when plotting graphs, the independent variable is plotted on the x-axis, and the dependent variable is plotted on the y-axis. You can read more about the practical skills involved in using graphs on page 41.

A straight-line graph has the form $y = mx + c$, where m is the gradient of the graph and c is a constant. In practical work, the aim is to rearrange the equation describing the relationship between the variables into this form. If the relationship is correct, then your plot will be a straight line. Plotting data in this form also allows anomalous points to be seen more easily.

Worked example

A student is using a model of a rollercoaster track (Figure 1) to investigate the relationship between the initial height of a ball on the track and its speed at the top of the loop.

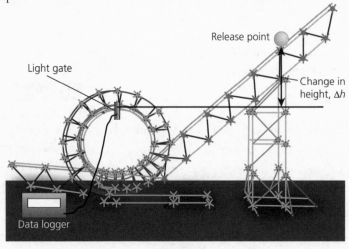

Figure 1

Exam tip

Current–voltage characteristics and Hooke's law graphs are often plotted with the dependent variable on the x-axis. This is convenient, as it makes the gradient equal to the constant of proportionality in each case (resistance and spring constant, respectively). Look carefully at the axes on graphs in case this has been done.

The student varies the initial height of the ball and measures the speed at the top of the loop using a light gate and data logging software. The initial energy of the ball is equal to its gravitational potential energy $E_p = mg\Delta h$. At the top of the loop, its kinetic energy is $E_k = \frac{1}{2}mv^2$.

a What quantities should the student plot in order to obtain a straight-line graph?

b What does the gradient of the graph represent?

Answer

a In this case, $\Delta E_k = \Delta E_p$, so she can write:

$$mg\Delta h = \frac{1}{2}mv^2$$

Rearranging to get an equation in the form of $y = mx + c$:

$$v^2 = 2g\Delta h$$

The student will need to plot v^2 (on the y-axis) against Δh (on the x-axis) to obtain a straight-line graph.

b The gradient is $m = 2g$, where g is the acceleration of free fall.

The gradient of any graph represents the change in y for a corresponding change in x:

$$\text{gradient} = \frac{\Delta y}{\Delta x}$$

This is a *rate of change*, and forms the basis of calculus.

To calculate the gradient from a straight-line graph, we draw a large triangle using the line of best fit as the hypotenuse of the triangle, as shown in Figure 2. In this case the gradient is equal to the rate of change of velocity with time $\left(\dfrac{\Delta v}{\Delta t}\right)$, or acceleration.

Exam tip

Some straight-line graphs will have no intercept on the y-axis, i.e. $y = mx$. Remember that only a graph such as this, which passes through the origin, shows that y is proportional to x.

Knowledge check 16

For the following relationships, state the quantities that need to be plotted to obtain a straight-line graph. In each case, state what is represented by the gradient of the graph.

a $c = f\lambda$ for variables f and λ

b $R = \dfrac{\rho l}{A}$ for variables R and l

c $T = 2\pi\sqrt{\dfrac{m}{k}}$ for variables T and m

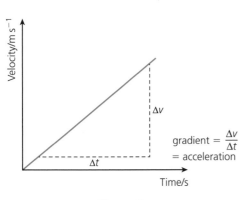

Figure 2

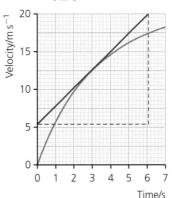

Figure 3

To calculate the gradient at a particular point from a curved graph, draw a tangent to the curve at that point. Then draw a large triangle using the tangent as the hypotenuse, as shown in Figure 3, and use this to calculate the gradient.

Mathematically, the gradient at a point is given by $\dfrac{dy}{dx}$ and can be found by differentiation.

Content Guidance

Figures 2 and 3 both show the motion of an object that is accelerating, but in Figure 3 the acceleration is changing. The gradient at a point represents the instantaneous acceleration of the object at that point. To calculate the average acceleration of the object, the readings over the whole of the graph need to be used.

As well as the gradient of a graph enabling us to determine a rate of change, the area under a graph may also have physical significance. In velocity–time graphs, such as Figures 2 and 3, the area under the graph represents the distance travelled. In order to calculate the appropriate area under the graph, your plot must include the origin.

Exam tip

When taking data from graphs, always read the units from the axes. Take care if they include prefixes, and make sure you use the correct values during your calculations.

(**A-level only**) Sometimes, it is helpful to plot data using logarithmic plots because the data cover a wide range of values. One way to do this is to use special log graph paper. Figure 5 shows the radioactive decay of strontium with time, plotted on log-linear paper. Although the decay is exponential, the graph is linear because the mass has been plotted on a logarithmic scale.

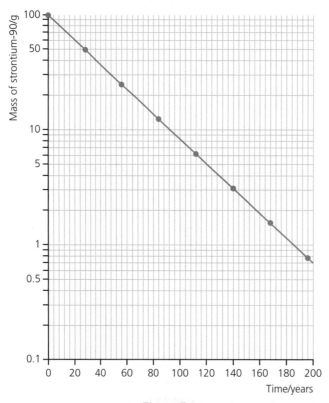

Figure 5

Instead of using special graph paper, a logarithmic plot of an exponential can also be drawn by taking natural logarithms ('ln' on your calculator) of both sides of the equation that describes the physical phenomenon.

Knowledge check 17

Using Figure 3, calculate the instantaneous acceleration of the object at 3 s, and the average acceleration of the object between 0 s and 6 s.

Knowledge check 18

State the physical quantity given by the area under each graph in Figure 4 and estimate the value of the quantity given by this area.

(a)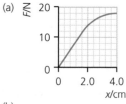

(b)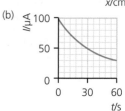

Figure 4

Worked example

(**A-level only**) A student measures the current, I, in a circuit as a capacitor discharges over time, t.

a What does she have to plot to obtain a straight-line graph?

b What do the intercept and gradient of the graph represent?

Answer

a The equation that describes the current is:

$$I = I_0 e^{-t/RC}$$

Taking natural logarithms ('ln') of both sides gives:

$$\ln I = \ln I_0 - \frac{t}{RC}$$

Plotting $\ln I$ against t will give a straight-line graph, because R and C are constants.

b The gradient is equal to $-\dfrac{1}{RC}$.

The intercept is equal to $\ln I_0$, where I_0 is the current at $t = 0$.

Figure 6 gives examples of the shapes of graphs for a range of different functions.

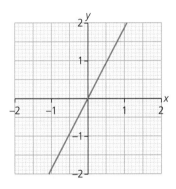

(a) Graph of $y = kx$, where k is a constant

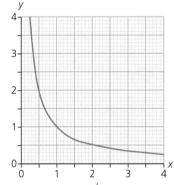

(b) Graph of $y = \dfrac{k}{x}$, where k is a constant

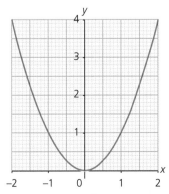

(c) Graph of $y = kx^2$, where k is a constant, in this case $k = 1$

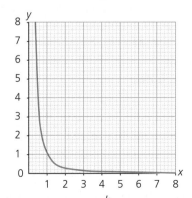

(d) Graph of $y = \dfrac{k}{x^2}$, where k is a constant, in this case $k = 1$

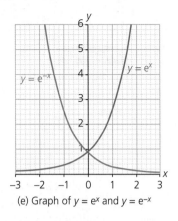

(e) Graph of $y = e^x$ and $y = e^{-x}$

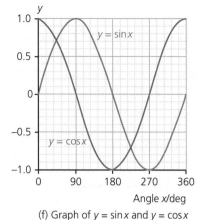

Angle x/deg

(f) Graph of $y = \sin x$ and $y = \cos x$

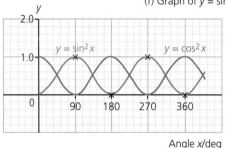

Angle x/deg

(g) Graph of $y = \sin^2 x$ and $y = \cos^2 x$

Figure 6

Geometry and trigonometry

Modelling the real world in physics requires us to solve problems in two (2D) or three (3D) dimensions. For example, we may need to think about forces acting at angles to one another; or the surface area of a solar panel normal to the sunlight.

Throughout your studies you will need to:

- use angles in regular 2D and 3D structures
- visualise and represent 2D and 3D forms, including 2D representations of 3D objects
- calculate areas of triangles, circumferences and areas of circles, and surface areas and volumes of rectangular blocks, cylinders and spheres
- use Pythagoras' theorem, and the angle sum of a triangle
- use sin, cos and tan in physical problems
- **use small-angle approximations, including:**
  - $\sin\theta \approx \theta$
  - $\tan\theta \approx \theta$
  - $\cos\theta \approx 1$ for small values of θ measured in radians
- understand the relationship between degrees and radians, and translate from one to the other

When doing practical work, or analysing data from practical work, you will often have to calculate different geometric properties of objects. Table 5 gives some useful formulae for this.

Table 5 Formulae for geometric properties

Calculation	Shape	Equation
Area under an F–x graph for a spring obeying Hooke's law	Triangle	area = $\frac{1}{2}$ × base × height
Cross-sectional area of a wire	Circle of radius r	area = πr^2
Energy radiated by an incandescent bulb	Sphere of radius r	surface area = $4\pi r^2$
Energy radiated by a fluorescent tube	Cylinder of radius r and height h	surface area = $2\pi r^2 + 2\pi rh$
Density of a block	Rectangular block of sides a, b and c	volume = $a \times b \times c$
Density of a marble	Sphere of radius r	volume = $\frac{4}{3}\pi r^3$
Volume of a gas cylinder	Cylinder of radius r and height h	volume = $\pi r^2 h$

When calculating the resultant of forces that are applied to an object, knowledge of trigonometry is essential.

Pythagoras' theorem states that if a right-angled triangle has sides a, b and c, where c is the hypotenuse, then $a^2 + b^2 = c^2$ (Figure 7). Right-angled triangles are also used to define the three functions sine, cosine and tangent.

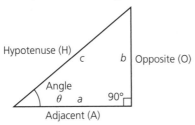

Figure 7

- $\sin\theta$ = opposite/hypotenuse
- $\cos\theta$ = adjacent/hypotenuse
- $\tan\theta$ = opposite/adjacent

Worked example

A student is investigating equilibrium using a force board similar to the one shown in Figure 8.

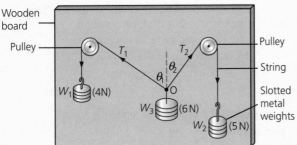

Figure 8

The system comes to rest with angles $\theta_1 = 57°$ and $\theta_2 = 42°$. Show that the system is in equilibrium.

Exam tip

Data are often given for the diameter of a circle or a sphere, instead of the radius. Remember that radius = ½ × diameter and so $r^2 = \frac{1}{4}d^2$.

Knowledge check 20

A copper pipe has an internal diameter of 12 mm and a length of 150 cm. Calculate the volume of liquid that can be contained in the pipe.

Knowledge check 21

The molar mass of carbon is 12.0 × 10^{-3} kg mol^{-1} and the density of diamond is 3500 kg m^{-3}. Estimate the atomic radius of a spherical carbon atom.

Exam tip

The sum of the internal angles in a triangle is 180°.

Answer

To be in equilibrium, the forces in each direction at point O (weight 3) must balance.

Resolving horizontally: $T_1 \sin \theta_1 = T_2 \sin \theta_2$

$T_1 \sin \theta_1 = 4\,\text{N} \sin 57° = 3.4\,\text{N}$ and $T_2 \sin \theta_2 = 5\,\text{N} \sin 42° = 3.3\,\text{N}$

We can see that the forces do not balance exactly. This is probably due to friction in the system causing experimental uncertainty.

Resolving vertically: $T_1 \cos \theta_1 + T_2 \cos \theta_2 = W_3$

$4\,\text{N} \cos 57° + 5\,\text{N} \cos 42° = 5.9\,\text{N}$

Once again, the vertical components balance to within a reasonable experimental error.

Degrees and radians are used to describe angles. In many cases, the radian is a useful measure, particularly when working with waves and oscillations.

A radian is defined as the angle created by the arc s of a circle that is equal in length to the radius r of the circle ($s = r$). Figure 9 shows that an angle θ in radians is given by $\theta = s/r$ or $s = r\theta$.

When using small angles, measured in radians, we can use the following **small-angle approximations** because the values are very similar:

$\sin \theta \approx \theta$

$\tan \theta \approx \theta$

$\cos \theta \approx 1$

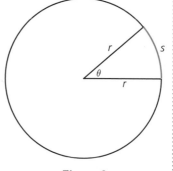

Figure 9

Practical skills

Physics is a practical subject, and experimental work should form a significant part of your AS or A-level physics course. It is commonly acknowledged that it is easier to learn and remember things if you have actually done them rather than having read about them or been told about them. That is why this section of the book is illustrated throughout by experiments, usually with a set of data for you to work through and questions to answer.

As you complete practical work during your physics course, you will develop skills in the use of a range of apparatus and techniques. Examination questions will test your knowledge and understanding of these techniques. You should refer to the specification, which contains a list of apparatus and techniques with which you should be familiar.

Exam tip

1 radian = 57.3°

Angle in radians = $\dfrac{\pi}{180°}$ × angle in degrees

Angle in degrees = $\dfrac{180°}{\pi}$ × angle in radians

Knowledge check 22

Express the following angles in radians to 3 s.f.: **a** 15.0°, **b** 50.0°, **c** 145°.

Knowledge check 23

Express the following angles in degrees to 3 s.f.: **a** $\pi/8$ rad, **b** 1.50 rad, **c** 0.150 rad.

Knowledge check 24

Calculate $\sin \theta$, $\cos \theta$ and $\tan \theta$ to 2 s.f. for the following angles: **a** 5.0 rad, **b** 0.50 rad, **c** 0.050 rad.

Exam tip

Make sure you have your calculator set in the right mode — degrees or radians — as required by the question.

Practical skills assessed in written papers

Examiners may ask you questions about your knowledge of scientific procedures or they may test your scientific knowledge set in a range of practical contexts. Although the focus will be on your knowledge of physics, without a good understanding of practical work you will find it difficult to answer this type of question. You will be expected to apply skills gained from the practical endorsement and will be required to describe and evaluate specific methods and procedures. These could include questions about alternative and unfamiliar methods for the experiments you may have carried out during your A-level physics course. This means that it is vital that you understand the practical aspects of your A-level physics course really well, so that you are able to plan, implement, analyse and evaluate experiments from every topic on the specification. The OCR A and OCR B (Advancing Physics) specifications state that question papers will assess the following practical skills:

1 Planning
  - experimental design, including solving problems set in a practical context
  - identifying variables that must be controlled
  - evaluating if an experimental method is appropriate to meet the expected outcomes

2 Implementing
  - using a wide range of practical apparatus and techniques correctly
  - using appropriate units for measurements
  - presenting observations and data in an appropriate format

3 Analysis
  - processing, analysing and interpreting qualitative and quantitative experimental results
  - using appropriate mathematical skills to analyse quantitative data
  - using significant figures appropriately
  - plotting and interpreting suitable graphs from experimental results, including selection and labelling of axes and measurement of gradients and intercepts

4 Evaluation
  - evaluating results and drawing conclusions
  - identifying anomalies in experimental measurements
  - identifying limitations in experimental procedures
  - using precision and accuracy of measurements and data, including margins of error, percentage errors and uncertainties in apparatus
  - refining experimental designs by suggesting improvements to the procedures and apparatus

About this section

For convenience, this section is in four main subsections, which reflect an orderly approach to practical work given in the specification:

  - Planning
  - Implementing
  - Analysing results
  - Evaluation

However, there will inevitably be a degree of overlap between each section.

Planning

Once the problem has been identified, you will be expected to produce a plan. Planning an experiment or investigation includes selecting appropriate equipment to make the relevant measurements. You will also need to describe measurement strategies and techniques to ensure accurate results. Safety issues must also be discussed.

Good experimental design

When planning an experiment, you should attempt to design a method that leads to the smallest uncertainties in your measurements. Exam questions may ask you to look at a number of factors:

- the resolution of the instruments used
- the manufacturer's tolerance on instruments and components such as resistors and capacitors
- how the experimenter uses the instrument's (e.g. parallax, zero error)
- the procedures adopted (e.g. repeated readings)

You may be required to evaluate procedures and explain how particular techniques could affect uncertainties in the measurements, or how the uncertainties could be reduced by using different apparatus or procedures.

Types of variables

You are expected to be able to identify variables, including those that must be controlled. You should be familiar with the following terminology:

- The *independent variable* is the variable for which values are changed by the experimenter.
- The *dependent variable* is the variable for which the value is measured for each and every change in the independent variable.
- *Control variables* may, in addition to the independent variable, affect the outcome of the investigation, and therefore have to be kept constant or at least monitored.

Worked example

A student investigates how the diameter of a ball bearing affects how long it takes to fall through a measuring cylinder filled with oil. What are the independent, dependent and control variables in this experiment?

Answer

Independent variable is diameter of ball bearing.

Dependent variable is time.

Control variables are temperature of oil, distance fallen, material of ball bearing, smoothness of ball bearing surface, type of oil and height of release of ball bearing.

Implementing

A key part of planning an experiment is describing how to obtain accurate and precise data. This involves choosing the most appropriate equipment and using it in such a way to enable the most accurate data to be obtained. This means that you will need to consider why data might not be accurate, and how to quantify the extent to which this affects any conclusions you can make from your data.

Errors

One of the specified requirements is that you should use precision and accuracy of measurements and data, including margins of error, percentage errors and uncertainties in apparatus.

An error is the difference between a measured result and the true value or accepted value, i.e. the value that would have been obtained in an ideal measurement (which is impossible to achieve!). With the exception of a fundamental constant, the true value is considered unknowable. An error can be due to random or systematic effects, and an error of unknown size is a source of *uncertainty*.

Random errors

There are always random errors present due to the way any instrument works, the way it is used or changes in the external conditions. The same measurement will give different values each time it is measured. The effect of this type of error can be reduced by taking repeat measurements and then averaging or by drawing a graph. Random errors produce scatter of the points around the line of best fit (Figure 10).

Random errors will give rise to an uncertainty in the measurement you have taken. It is important to be able to estimate the uncertainty in a measurement so that its effect can be taken into consideration when drawing conclusions about experimental results.

Systematic errors

A systematic error produces measurements that are consistently too large or too small by the same amount. This could be caused by recording the wrong unit, poor technique (e.g. systematically reading from a scale at an angle, causing parallax error), failure to check for zero error, or incorrect calibration of the instrument.

Zero error

A zero error occurs when the measuring instrument is not set on zero accurately. The zero error should be subtracted from or added to each measured reading to give the true value (Figure 11).

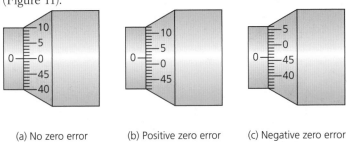

(a) No zero error   (b) Positive zero error   (c) Negative zero error

Figure 11

Sometimes a systematic error is not apparent from the measurements. Another advantage of drawing a graph is that it can indicate if there is a systematic error and enable you to make allowance for it (Figure 12).

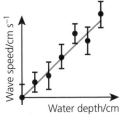

Figure 10

Knowledge check 25

State three possible sources of random error in an experiment.

Exam tip

Before an instrument is used to make a measurement, it is important to check for zero error. This is an example of a systematic error, which will cause a constant error in all the readings.

Knowledge check 26

The thickness of a sheet of glass is measured to be 0.86 mm using the micrometer shown in Figure 11b. What is the actual thickness of the glass?

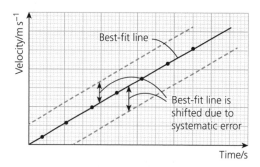

Figure 12

A systematic error will be seen on a graph by the line of best fit being shifted up or down the *y*-axis because each measurement is larger or smaller than the true value by the same amount. A systematic error does *not* affect the *gradient* of the line of best fit but simply alters the *y*-intercept.

Accuracy and precision

In everyday English, *accuracy* and *precision* have similar meanings, but in physics this is not the case.

A measured value is considered to be *accurate* if it is judged to be close to the true value. The 'true value' of a measurement is the value that would be obtained in an ideal world. However, any actual measurement you make will always be subject to random and systematic errors.

The term *precision* denotes the consistency between values obtained by repeated measurements — a measurement is precise if the values 'cluster' together. Precision is influenced only by random errors. We can try to ascertain and quantify these errors, i.e. *estimate the uncertainty* in our value. Precise results would show little scatter around the line of best fit on a graph but might have a systematic error making them inaccurate. Accuracy and precision are summarised in Figure 13.

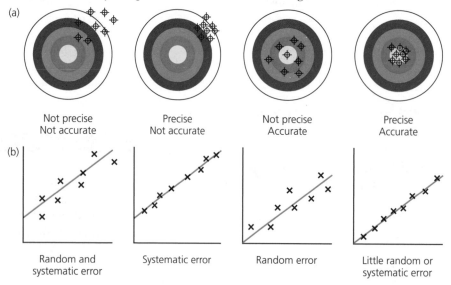

Figure 13

Knowledge check 27

Explain the difference between accuracy and precision.

Knowledge check 28

The magnetic field strength of the Earth at a point on the Earth's surface was measured five times and gave the following values: 50 mT, 48 mT, 46 mT, 52 mT, 62 mT. The true value of the magnetic field strength at this point was known to be 51 mT. Comment on the precision of these data.

Uncertainty in measurements

Every measurement has an inherent uncertainty due to the resolution of the instrument, manufacturing error, the way the instrument is used (human error!) or the design of the experiment.

An uncertainty for a single reading, or repeated readings that are the same, will be at least half the **resolution** of the instrument. For repeated readings that are different, the uncertainty can be taken as being *half the range* of the readings.

As a general guide, the uncertainty of a **reading** is at least ±0.5 of the resolution. A reading is a value found from a single judgement, e.g. when reading a thermometer, Geiger counter, top-pan balance, measuring cylinder, or ruler with a zero end. For such 'analogue' devices, it may be possible to interpolate to the nearest half a division on the scale (Figure 14).

The uncertainty of a **measurement** is at least ±1 of the resolution. A measurement requires the value to be taken from two readings or judgements, e.g. when using a non-zero-ended ruler (the start and the end readings), a stopwatch (start and stop) or the extension of a spring (original and final lengths).

Figure 14

> **Exam tip**
>
> When using an analogue instrument, always try to interpolate between whole divisions, e.g. to the nearest 0.5 mm on a ruler or to 0.1 degrees for a thermometer calibrated in degrees.

> **Exam tip**
>
> In exam papers, values will often be stated together with the absolute uncertainty, e.g. 'a wire has a diameter of 1.87 mm ± 0.01 mm'. The uncertainty should be quoted to be the same number of decimal places as the reading.

> **Worked example**
>
> Estimate the uncertainty in a length measurement of 122 mm made using the ruler shown in Figure 15, and write down how the length should be recorded.
>
>
>
> **Figure 15**
>
> **Answer**
>
> The smallest division on the ruler is 1 mm. Therefore, the uncertainty in each reading is $\frac{1}{2} \times 1$ mm = 0.5 mm.
>
> But as we are taking readings at each end, we are making two judgements. So the total uncertainty in this measurement of length would be ±(2 × 0.5 mm) = ±1 mm.
>
> Length = 122 mm ± 1 mm.

> **Knowledge check 29**
>
> What is meant by the resolution of an instrument?

Other factors affecting the uncertainty in a measurement

The general guidelines above give the *smallest* uncertainty in a measurement or reading. Often the resolution of the instrument is not the limiting factor, and the way the instrument is used can lead to larger uncertainties. The instrument's resolution allows us to assess the *minimum* possible uncertainty. You need to make an assessment of the other factors, such as the set-up and use of the apparatus, and take these into account.

In experiments, you will often be timing events or measuring the length of something. The following examples should help you understand how the uncertainties involved are actually much larger than those due to the resolution of the stopwatch or ruler.

A stopwatch typically has a resolution of 0.01 s, but the reaction time of the person using it is likely to be no quicker than 0.05 s or 0.10 s. You should record the full reading on the stopwatch (e.g. 18.62 s) and reduce this to a more appropriate number of significant figures at a later stage, e.g. after averaging readings.

If you are measuring the length of a piece of an unstretched elastic band, it is very difficult to place the elastic completely straight against the ruler. This could lead to an uncertainty of ±2 or ±3 mm.

The uncertainty of the reading from digital voltmeters and ammeters depends on the tolerance quoted by the manufacturer (which may be considerable). If this is not known then the reading should usually be stated to ±1 in the last digit when quoting the value and the uncertainty.

Worked example

Estimate the uncertainty in the reading of potential difference (p.d.) shown in Figure 16, and state how you would record the value of the p.d. The dial is set on the 20 V dc scale.

Answer

The uncertainty will be ± the smallest division shown on the meter = ±0.01 V.

The reading is therefore 19.16 V ± 0.01 V.

The manufacturing tolerance is not stated, so by quoting the uncertainty to ± the smallest division, we are making a best possible estimate.

Figure 16

Percentage uncertainties

It is very useful to be able to quote uncertainties as percentages. This also enables uncertainties to be combined easily.

$$\text{percentage uncertainty} = \frac{\text{uncertainty}}{\text{value}} \times 100\%$$

The digital voltmeter shown in Figure 16 is being used to measure the p.d. across a lamp. Estimate the percentage uncertainty in the reading of 19.16 V.

Answer

The uncertainty will be ± the smallest division shown on the meter = ±0.01 V.

The reading is therefore 19.16 V ± 0.01 V.

Percentage uncertainty = (0.01 V/19.16 V) × 100% = 0.05%.

The manufacturing tolerance is not stated, so by quoting the uncertainty to ± the smallest division we are making a best possible estimate.

Combining uncertainties

In experiments, measurements are often made using several instruments and are then used to calculate a quantity. The combined uncertainty can be found as follows:

- If quantities are added or subtracted, *add* the *absolute* uncertainties of each quantity.
- If quantities are multiplied or divided, *add* the *percentage* uncertainties of each quantity.
- If a quantity is raised to a power, then *multiply* the *percentage* uncertainty by the *power*.

Worked example

The p.d. across a bulb is measured to be 3.15 V when the current in it is 40.8 mA.
a Calculate the power.
b Estimate the percentage uncertainty in the power.
c State how the power should be recorded.

Answer

a Power = VI = 3.15 V × 40.8 × 10^{-3} A = 0.129 W (data to 3 s.f., and so the answer should be to 3 s.f.).
b The p.d. and current are both *readings*, so the uncertainty is *theoretically* half the smallest division, but in practice we take it to be the smallest division to make some allowance for manufacturing tolerance of the digital meters. In this case, 0.01 V and 0.1 mA. (We shall often write '% uc' as shorthand for percentage uncertainty.)
So, % uc in V = (0.01 V/3.15 V) × 100% = 0.317%
and % uc in I = (0.1 mA/40.8 mA) × 100% = 0.245%
This gives % uc in P = % uc in V + % uc in I
so % uc in P = 0.317% + 0.245% = 0.562% = 0.6%
c Uncertainty in P = 0.562% of 0.129 W = 7.2 × 10^{-4} W ≈ 0.001 W
Power = 0.129 W ± 0.001 W or 129 mW ± 1 mW

Making measurements

There are different procedures that can be used to reduce error and uncertainty in measurements. When choosing how to measure different quantities, you also need to decide what you will do to reduce the uncertainties.

Parallax error

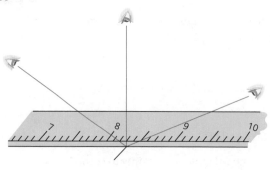

Figure 17

When reading a scale, for example from an analogue meter or ruler, you should ensure that the pointer, the scale and your eye are all in line. This will avoid *parallax error*. It is important not to look at the scale from an angle, as this would give a measurement that is larger or smaller than the true value (Figure 17).

Using a vernier scale

Vernier callipers and micrometers enable measurements of length or thickness to be made to a much greater resolution than using a ruler and can reduce the uncertainty by a factor of 10 or 100, respectively. Often you will be able to use electronic or digital instruments, which have an even greater resolution.

Vernier callipers measure to the nearest 0.1 mm and therefore measure to a precision of 1% or better if used to measure lengths of 1 cm or longer. Figure 18 shows how to read the scale — a hand lens is recommended, as the scale lines can be difficult to see:

- the zero on the vernier scale is just beyond the 21 mm mark on the main scale
- locate the lines on the main scale and the vernier scale that are *exactly lined up with each other*
- in this case this is the '5' on the vernier scale
- the reading is therefore 21.5 mm

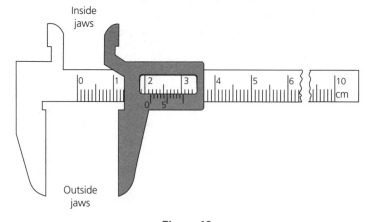

Figure 18

> **Knowledge check 32**
>
> **a** Figure 17 shows an enlarged millimetre scale. What is the correct reading?
> **b** Explain how a mirror can be used to reduce parallax error when taking a reading from an analogue scale that has a pointer.

> **Knowledge check 33**
>
> What does the vernier scale shown in Figure 19 read?

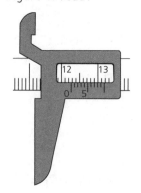

Figure 19

The following example shows how, by using a vernier scale and a sensitive electronic balance, the accuracy of the measurements of length and mass, and therefore the determination of density, can be improved. This is particularly important when a quantity is being squared or cubed.

Worked example

a A student is asked to determine the density of aluminium in the form of a cylinder. He measures the diameter and length of the cylinder with a metre rule and the mass with a top pan balance. He records the following measurements:

length = 75 ± 1 mm

diameter = 25 ± 1 mm

mass = 98.8 ± 0.1 g

Use these data to determine the student's value for the density of aluminium and estimate the percentage uncertainty in his value.

b His teacher suggests that he would get a more accurate value for the density if he used vernier callipers to measure the diameter and length.

What does the teacher mean by 'accurate'? Estimate the improvement to the accuracy this would make.

Answer

a volume = $\pi r^2 h = \pi \times (12.5 \times 10^{-3} \text{ m})^2 \times 75 \times 10^{-3} \text{ m} = 3.68 \times 10^{-5} \text{ m}^3$

density = mass/volume = $98.8 \times 10^{-3} \text{ kg}/3.68 \times 10^{-5} \text{ m}^3$

= $2.7 \times 10^3 \text{ kg m}^{-3}$ (2 s.f. in line with the data)

% uc in d = (1 mm/25 mm) × 100% = 4.0%

so % uc in r^2 = % uc in d^2 = 2 × % uc in d = 2 × 4.0% = 8.0%

% uc in h = (1 mm/75 mm) × 100% = 1.3%

% uc in m = (0.1 g/98.8 g) × 100% = 0.1%

so % uc in density = 8.0% + 1.3% + 0.1% = 9.4% ≈ 9%

b An accurate value is one that is close to the true value.

A vernier scale will have a resolution of 0.1 mm compared with 1 mm for the rule. The percentage uncertainties in d and h will therefore be 0.40% and 0.13%, respectively.

The percentage uncertainty in the density will then be (2 × 0.40% + 0.13% + 0.10%) = 1.03% ≈ 1%.

This means the accuracy will be improved by a factor of about nine times.

Knowledge check 34

Calculate the density of a marble having a diameter of 10 mm and a mass of 1.3 g. Give your answer in kg m^{-3} and in g cm^{-3}.

Exam tip

When a quantity is raised to the power of n, the *percentage* uncertainty in the quantity is multiplied by n.

Using a micrometer

A micrometer (Figure 20) has a resolution of ±0.01 mm. The micrometer should be closed using the ratchet until it *just* clicks.

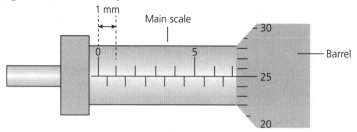

Figure 20

When using a micrometer, remember the following:

- Do not over-tighten, as this could squash the object and/or damage the thread. Use the ratchet to close the jaws.
- Check for a zero error and add or subtract as necessary.
- Make sure you read the scale correctly (in particular, whether the main scale reading is less than or more than 0.5 mm).
- Measure the diameter several times and in several places to check for uniformity. (For a wire, for example, you could measure the diameter at each end and in the middle to check if the wire is thinner at one end. You could also then take readings at right angles to check that the wire has a circular cross-sectional area.)

Repeated measurements

Random errors are generally caused either by human misjudgements, e.g. reaction time and interpolating between scale divisions, or by variations in a measurement, e.g. non-uniformity of a wire. Random errors will cause measurements to spread about a mean value. Because precise measurements are measurements in which there is very little spread about the mean value, you must try to reduce random errors in order to improve precision.

Because random errors are likely to cause readings to be larger than the true value as often as smaller than the true value, repeating readings or measurements will smooth out the effect of random errors.

For repeat measurements:

$$\text{percentage uncertainty} = \frac{\frac{1}{2} \times \text{range}}{\text{mean value}} \times 100\%$$

By plotting a graph, the line of best fit will effectively average out the random errors, but they can never be eliminated completely. You will also be able to see the scatter of the points about the line of best fit and so see how precise the measurements are.

Knowledge check 35

a What is the resolution of the main scale of the micrometer shown in Figure 20?

b What is the thickness of the object being measured by the micrometer shown in Figure 20? What assumption are you making?

Exam tip

You should be able to state the precautions that should be taken to improve accuracy when using a micrometer.

Knowledge check 36

A micrometer has a zero error of +0.03 mm. A student measures the diameter of a pencil lead to be 2.12 mm. What is the actual diameter of the lead?

Worked example

The resistance of a thermistor was measured three times at 20°C giving values of $670\,\Omega$, $661\,\Omega$ and $678\,\Omega$. Calculate the percentage uncertainty in the value of the resistance, and state how the resistance of the thermistor should be recorded.

Answer

range $= 678 - 661 = 17\,\Omega$

mean $= (670 + 661 + 678)/3 = 669.7\,\Omega = 670\,\Omega$ (3 s.f.)

$$\% \text{ uc} = \frac{\left(\frac{1}{2} \times 17\right)\Omega}{670\,\Omega} \times 100\% = 1.27\%$$

1.27% of $669.7\,\Omega = 8.5\,\Omega \Rightarrow R = 670\,\Omega \pm 9\,\Omega$

Exam tip

Improving precision: you need to be able to describe how the measurements obtained from an experiment can be made more precise.

Worked example

For an angle of incidence of 40.0° on a glass block, the angle of refraction was measured three times as 25.5°, 25.0° and 26.0°. How should the mean value of the angle of refraction be expressed?

Answer

range $= 26.0° - 25.0° = 1.0°$

mean $= (25.5° + 25.0° + 26.0°)/3 = 76.5°/3 = 25.5°$

angle of refraction $= 25.5° \pm 0.5°$

Knowledge check 37

Explain how the precision of experimental measurements can be improved.

Worked example

Measuring the density of glass and sand

We can illustrate a number of the points we have made concerning good experimental design by considering an experiment to investigate whether some glass might be manufactured from sand. The following apparatus is used: glass block, plastic cup, dry sand, 250 ml measuring cylinder, vernier callipers and access to an electronic balance and water.

The experiment is carried out as follows.

For the glass block:

■ Using the vernier callipers, the dimensions are determined as:

$l = (116.0 \pm 0.2)\,\text{mm}$

$w = (63.0 \pm 0.2)\,\text{mm}$

$h = (48.7 \pm 0.2)\,\text{mm}$

■ Using the electronic balance:

mass $= 882.4 \pm 0.1\,\text{g}$

For the sand:

- Using the electronic balance:

  mass of empty plastic cup = 35.5 ± 0.1 g

  mass of cup and sand = 87.1 ± 0.1 g

- The measuring cylinder is filled with $100\,\text{cm}^3$ of water and then the sand is added.

  volume of the water + sand = $123\,\text{cm}^3$

a Determine the densities of glass and sand.

b Estimate the uncertainties in each of these values.

c Make a comparison between your final values with reference to these uncertainties.

d Write a conclusion discussing the extent to which your results support the fact that glass is made from sand.

e Explain any experimental techniques that you would use in the above experiment to try to reduce the uncertainty in the measurements.

Answer

a *Glass:*

volume = $116.0 \times 10^{-3}\,\text{m} \times 63.0 \times 10^{-3}\,\text{m} \times 48.7 \times 10^{-3}\,\text{m}$

$\qquad = 3.56 \times 10^{-4}\,\text{m}^3$

density = mass/volume = $882.4 \times 10^{-3}\,\text{kg}/3.56 \times 10^{-4}\,\text{m}^3$

$\qquad = 2.48 \times 10^3\,\text{kg m}^{-3}$ or $2.48\,\text{g cm}^{-3}$

Sand:

volume of sand = $(123 - 100)\,\text{cm}^3 = 23\,\text{cm}^3 \pm 2\,\text{cm}^3$ (as we have two readings)

mass of sand = $(87.1 - 35.5)\,\text{g} = 51.6\,\text{g} \pm 0.2\,\text{g}$

density = mass/volume = $51.6\,\text{g}/23\,\text{cm}^3$

$\qquad = 2.2\,\text{g cm}^{-3}$ (to 2 s.f. as volume is only to 2 s.f.)

b *Glass:*

% uc in mass = $(0.1\,\text{g}/882.4\,\text{g}) \times 100\% = 0.01\%$

% uc in volume = % uc in length + % uc in width + % uc in depth

$\qquad = (0.17 + 0.32 + 0.41)\% = 0.90\%$

% uc in density = % uc in mass + % uc in volume

$\qquad = (0.01 + 0.90)\% = 0.91\%$

Uncertainty in density = 0.91% of $2.48\,\text{g cm}^{-3} = \pm 0.02\,\text{g cm}^{-3}$

→

Sand:

% uc in density = % uc in mass + % uc in volume

$$= (0.2\,g/51.6\,g) \times 100\% + (2\,cm^3/23\,cm^3) \times 100\%$$

$$= (0.4 + 8.7)\% = 9.1\%$$

Uncertainty in density = 9.1% of $2.2\,g\,cm^{-3}$ = $\pm 0.2\,g\,cm^{-3}$

c The percentage difference between the density of glass and the density of sand is:

$$\frac{(2.48 - 2.2)\,g\,cm^{-3}}{2.34\,g\,cm^{-3}} \times 100\% = 12\%$$

d The minimum value that the density of the glass could have is $2.46\,g\,cm^{-3}$ and the maximum possible value for the sand is $2.4\,g\,cm^{-3}$.

Because the values do not quite overlap, the 12% difference cannot be accounted for by the experimental uncertainties, suggesting that glass may *not* be made entirely from sand. More likely reasons for the discrepancy are that the sand may not have been completely dry initially, or not all the air between the sand particles was replaced by water in the measuring cylinder.

> **Exam tip**
>
> The percentage difference between two experimental values is given by:
>
> $$\%difference = \frac{\text{difference between the values}}{\text{average of the two values}} \times 100\%$$
>
> The percentage difference between an experimental value and a stated or known value is given by:
>
> $$\%difference = \frac{\text{difference between the values}}{\text{stated value}} \times 100\%$$

e You might suggest the following:
- Check the vernier for zero error.
- Repeat measurements of block dimensions in at least two different places for each dimension and average.
- Shake the sand well to prevent air pockets.
- Keep your eye level with the water meniscus to prevent parallax error.

Knowledge check 38

Explain how you would determine, as accurately as possible, the volume of a glass marble.

Multiple readings

The use of multiple readings reduces the uncertainty. For example, if you determine the thickness of one sheet of paper by measuring the thickness of 50 sheets in a stack, and dividing by 50, you will then reduce the uncertainty in the measurement of one sheet by a factor of 50. In general, the uncertainty of each measurement will be the uncertainty of the whole measurement divided by the number of instances (e.g. sheets of paper or oscillations of a pendulum). This method works because the *percentage* uncertainty in the value of the thickness of one sheet will be the same as the percentage uncertainty in the measurement of multiple sheets.

Worked example

The thickness of ten sheets of paper is measured with a micrometer (resolution ±0.01 mm) and is found to be 1.08 mm. What is the percentage uncertainty in the mean thickness of one sheet?

Compare this to a measurement of the thickness of a ream of 500 sheets made using a vernier (resolution ±0.1 mm), which is 55.1 mm.

Answer

Thickness of ten sheets of paper: 1.08 mm ± 0.01 mm = 1.08 mm ± 0.9%

Mean thickness of one sheet of paper = 1.08 mm/10 = 0.108 mm ± 0.9%

Thickness of ream of 500 sheets = 55.1 mm ± 0.1 mm = 55.1 mm ± 0.18%

Mean thickness of one sheet = 55.1 mm/500 = 0.110 mm ± 0.18%

By measuring 500 sheets, the percentage uncertainty in the mean thickness of one sheet is reduced by a factor of 5.

This technique is particularly useful when applied to timing. For example, by timing over multiple oscillations, the overall uncertainty will be reduced significantly and the effect of your reaction time will become less significant.

Worked example

Figure 21 shows a stopwatch reading for 20 oscillations of a simple pendulum.

- a What is the resolution of the instrument?
- b Discuss what a realistic estimate of the uncertainty in this time would be.
- c Explain why it is an advantage to time 20 oscillations when determining the period T of the oscillations.
- d Determine a value for the period T and the estimated uncertainty in your value.
- e Compare this uncertainty with that which would be incurred if only one oscillation had been timed.

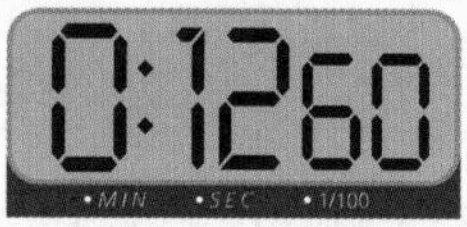

Figure 21

Answer

- a The resolution of the stopwatch is ±0.01 s.
- b This is insignificant compared to human reaction time, which is at least 0.05 s. As this applies both when starting and stopping the timing, it would be appropriate to use ±0.1 s as the uncertainty in the measurement of time using a stopwatch.
- c By measuring the time for 20 oscillations, and then dividing by 20, you would reduce the uncertainty by a factor of 20, as the error only occurs when the stopwatch is started and stopped.

→

Knowledge check 39

- a Why is the resolution of a stopwatch (0.01 s) not used when determining the uncertainty of timing an event taking about 3 s?
- b Suggest a suitable uncertainty for a single such event.

Exam tip

The absolute uncertainty in a measurement made with a metre ruler is about 1 mm. Provided lengths in excess of 100 mm are measured, then the percentage uncertainty will be less than 1%.

Exam tip

Always record the actual instrument reading and round up or down later.

d $20T = 12.60\,\text{s} \Rightarrow T = 0.630\,\text{s}$

Estimated uncertainty is the reaction time of 0.1 s:

% uc in timing = $(0.1\,\text{s}/12.60\,\text{s}) \times 100\% = 0.8\% = \%$ uc in T

uncertainty in $T = 0.8\% \times 0.630\,\text{s} = 0.005\,\text{s} \Rightarrow T = 0.630 \pm 0.005\,\text{s}$

e If only one oscillation was timed, measured T would be $0.63 \pm 0.10\,\text{s}$:

% uc in $T = (0.1\,\text{s}/0.63\,\text{s}) \times 100\% = 16\%$

(This is 20 times as much as the percentage uncertainty when timing 20 oscillations.)

Exam tip

Timing 20 oscillations and then dividing by 20 to find the time period reduces the uncertainty by a factor of 20.

Using a set-square to reduce uncertainty

A set-square can be particularly useful when determining precise measurements, as shown in Figure 22.

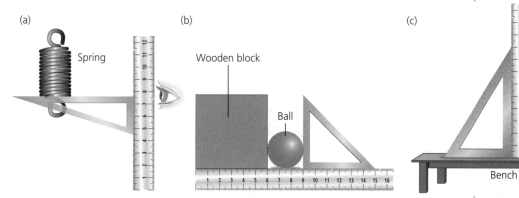

(a)   Spring

(b)   Wooden block   Ball

(c)   Bench

Figure 22

Make sure you keep your eye level, as shown in Figure 22a. To make sure that a clamped ruler is vertical in relation to the bench (Figure 22c), a plumb-line can be used instead — a small metal bob on a piece of string will hang vertically if suspended freely. This can be clamped next to the ruler.

Knowledge check 40

A mass on a spring completes 10 oscillations in 18.9 s. Determine the percentage uncertainty in the time period suggested by the precision of the recorded data.

Worked example

Determining the spring constant of a spring

You are asked to investigate the limit of proportionality and determine the spring constant of a spring. Describe how you would do this. Your answer should include:

■ a list of apparatus

■ a diagram of the experimental set-up

■ an outline of the procedure (including safety considerations)

■ what you could do to reduce the uncertainty in your measurements of length and extension

Knowledge check 41

Explain how you could use a set-square to check that a beam is horizontal with respect to the bench.

→

Answer

Apparatus: retort stand and clamp, metre rule, set-square, slotted masses and hanger, spring

Set-up: Figure 23 shows how the apparatus is set up.

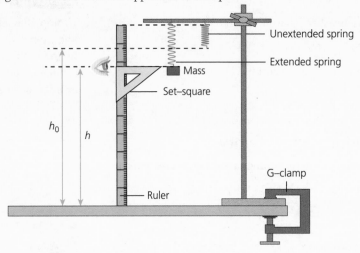

Figure 23

Safety considerations:

■ Attach the masses securely to the spring and ensure that, should the masses fall, they will not fall on your feet. You may need to protect the floor with a crash pad.

■ The clamp stand must be securely attached to the bench with a G-clamp.

Method:

■ Secure the ruler as close to the spring as possible and use the set-square to ensure that the rule is vertical.

■ Read the position of the bottom coil of the spring, using the set-square to ensure that the line between the spring and the ruler is horizontal.

■ Align the eye with the top of the set-square to avoid parallax error.

■ Add the mass hanger and masses one at a time and read the new position of the bottom ring each time until the extension is no longer linear.

■ For each reading, calculate the extension of the spring by subtracting the original reading h_0 from the new reading h.

Using trigonometry to measure small angles

At best, a protractor can measure to 0.5° by interpolating between divisions. For an angle of, say, 5° this would give rise to an uncertainty of 10%. By using trigonometric methods to measure small angles, we can significantly reduce this uncertainty. If you can measure the adjacent and opposite sides of a triangle using a ruler, as shown in Figure 24, then the angle can be calculated using $\theta = \tan^{-1}$ (opposite/adjacent) $= \tan^{-1}(h/l)$.

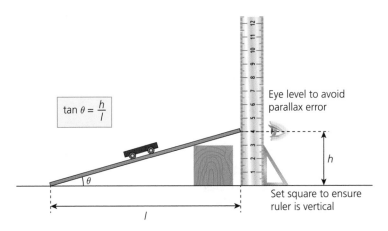

Figure 24

Techniques for timing oscillations

Often, in experiments, the uncertainty in a reading is due not so much to the measuring instrument itself but rather to how it is used. There are a number of experiments at AS and A-level that require you to time an object that is oscillating.

Precautions to take when timing oscillations:

- Take care not to miscount oscillations — say 'nought' when starting to time.
- Use a *fiducial marker* (i.e. a pointer) behind the object to help you judge when the oscillating object passes the centre/equilibrium position (Figure 25). The speed of the oscillator is fastest as it passes through the equilibrium position, so you should time from this point. If you try to time from the maximum displacement, the object will be moving very slowly and it will be very difficult to judge when it has actually reached the point of maximum displacement and is about to reverse direction.

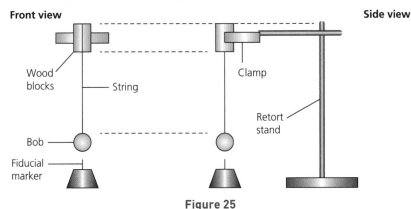

Figure 25

- Only start timing once the object has completed one or two oscillations. This will help you to start timing at the correct point. It will also ensure that you have not affected the motion of the object by giving it a small push at the start.
- Try to time at least 20 oscillations, if you can, in order to reduce the uncertainty. Obviously, if the system is heavily damped, then this will be difficult as the amplitude of the oscillations will decrease rapidly. In this case, take proportionately more repeat readings.

Oscillations of a metre rule

A student makes some measurements of the time period T of the oscillations of a wooden metre rule in order to find a value for the Young modulus of the wood, using the arrangement shown in Figure 26. She finds in a textbook that the Young modulus E for the wood is given by the formula

$$E = \frac{16\pi^2 ML^3}{wt^3 T^2}$$

where M is the mass suspended from the rule at a horizontal distance L from where the rule is clamped, and w and t are the width and thickness of the rule, respectively.

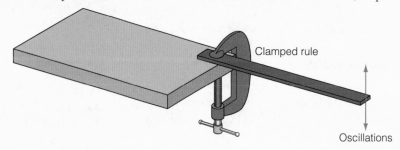

Figure 26

She plans to use:

- **two 100 g slotted masses** attached using elastic bands to either side of the rule, near the end, to make L as long as possible — with the slots in the masses perpendicular to the rule so that she can read the scale to determine the position of the centre of mass
- **a digital stopwatch** to time the oscillations — one that can record to a resolution of 0.01 s, which she considers to be more than adequate for timings that are likely to be of the order of 10 s
- **vernier callipers** to measure the width and thickness of the rule, at different points along its length — the callipers can read to a resolution of 0.1 mm
- a pin secured to the metre rule with a small piece of modelling clay to act as a **fiducial marker** to help her judge the centre of the oscillations

She records the following results:

$M = 200 \text{ g}$

$L = 937 - 40 = 897 \text{ mm}$

$w = 28.5, 28.0, 28.6, 28.9 \text{ mm}$; average 28.5 mm

$t = 6.6, 6.7, 6.6, 6.6 \text{ mm}$; average 6.6 mm

$20T = 8.59, 8.54, 8.18, 8.61 \text{ s}$; average 8.48 s

a Explain why a value of 8.58 s for the average time should be used rather than the value stated by the student.

b Show that these data give a value of the order of 10^{10} Pa for the Young modulus of the wood.

→

c Explain the number of significant figures to which the final value should be given.

d Suggest a suitable uncertainty for the value of the period *T*.

e Discuss whether the selection of vernier callipers, which could only be read to a precision of 0.1 mm, to measure the width and thickness of the rule, was an *appropriate strategy*. Justify your answer by estimating the percentage uncertainty that these measurements introduce into the value obtained for the Young modulus.

f To what extent would using a micrometer screw gauge, or digital callipers, reading to 0.01 mm, reduce the percentage uncertainty in the value obtained for the Young modulus?

Answer

a Looking at the four values for 20*T*, it would appear that the 8.18 reading is anomalous because it is about 0.5 s smaller than the other values (suggesting only 19 oscillations may have been counted). This value should therefore be ignored (with a note to this effect) when determining the average value.

b Care needs to be exercised with units — all of the measurements need to be converted to SI units:

$$M = 0.200\,\text{kg}$$

$$L = 0.897\,\text{m}$$

$$w = 28.5 \times 10^{-3}\,\text{m}$$

$$t = 6.6 \times 10^{-3}\,\text{m}$$

$$T = 8.58\,\text{s} \div 20 = 0.429\,\text{s}$$

so:

$$E = \frac{16\pi^2 ML^3}{wt^3 T^2} = \frac{16\pi^2 \times 0.200\,\text{kg} \times (0.897\,\text{m})^3}{28.5 \times 10^{-3}\,\text{m} \times (6.6 \times 10^{-3}\,\text{m})^3 \times (0.429\,\text{s})^2}$$

$$= 1.5 \times 10^{10}\,\text{Pa} \sim 10^{10}\,\text{Pa}$$

c The value should be quoted to 2 s.f., $1.5 \times 10^{10}\,\text{Pa}$, because this is the number of significant figures of the least precise measurement — the thickness of the rule, 6.6 mm, has been measured to only 2 s.f.

d Although the time taken for 20 oscillations has been recorded to a precision of 0.01 s, the range of values is $(8.61 - 8.54)\,\text{s} = 0.07\,\text{s}$. This is probably slightly less than the human reaction time. A more realistic uncertainty in 20*T* would be 0.1 s. This would give an uncertainty for the value of *T* of $0.1 \div 20 = 5\,\text{ms}$. We can then say $T = 0.429 \pm 0.005\,\text{s}$.

e The measurements recorded for the width were:

$$w = 28.5, 28.0, 28.6, 28.9\,\text{mm; average } 28.5\,\text{mm}$$

The range of values is therefore $(28.9 - 28.0)\,\text{mm} = 0.9\,\text{mm}$.
If we use half the range (0.45 mm) as our uncertainty, we get:

$$\%\text{ uc in } w = \frac{0.45\,\text{mm}}{28.5\,\text{mm}} \times 100\% = 1.6\%$$

→

> **Exam tip**
>
> Results that are clearly anomalous should be ignored when calculating the average of several values, and the fact that you have done this should be stated. Note that one advantage of taking repeat readings is that an anomalous reading can be spotted and allowed for.

Using a vernier scale reading to a precision of 0.1 mm to measure a thickness of 6.6 mm means that there is a percentage uncertainty in t of:

$$\frac{0.1\,\text{mm}}{6.6\,\text{mm}} \times 100\% = 1.5\%$$

Because the term t^3 occurs in the formula for the Young modulus, the percentage uncertainty introduced by this measurement will be $3 \times 1.5\% = 4.5\%$.

The combined contribution of the measurements for width and thickness is therefore:

$$\% \text{ uc} = 1.6\% + 4.5\% = 6.1\%$$

This is a not insignificant uncertainty. A vernier only reading to 0.1 mm to measure the thickness was not a good choice.

f   If an instrument reading to 0.01 mm had been used, the percentage uncertainty in the thickness would have been reduced by a factor of 10, giving an uncertainty due to this measurement of less than 0.5%, which is perfectly acceptable. However, due to the relatively large spread of values in the measurement of the width, using a more sensitive instrument would not have had much effect on the previously calculated uncertainty of 1.6%. The overall uncertainty would therefore be about 2%, which is nevertheless a considerable improvement.

Using data loggers

Data loggers record data automatically and can record data with very small intervals or over long periods of time. They can record thousands of measurements per second, with the data output displayed on a computer as a graph or in a table. The number of readings taken per second is called the *sample rate*. Sensors are available to enable a wide range of measurements to be made, e.g. force, current, potential difference, magnetic flux density and temperature. The data logger is able to measure several variables simultaneously and so can, for example, record how force varies with time. This graph could then be used to calculate the impulse by determining the area underneath the line.

Worked example

In an experiment to investigate how the current changes with time as a capacitor is charged, a data logger attached to a current sensor is used instead of a digital ammeter and stopwatch. State three advantages of using a data logger in this way.

Answer

You could state:

- eliminates reaction time errors
- automatically takes current and time readings simultaneously
- updates the display much quicker than a standard ammeter
- high sample rate and so records many readings of current per second
- immediately measures the initial current the instant the experiment is started
- the data are stored in a computer and so can be easily processed and analysed (e.g. the gradient or area under a graph calculated)

Knowledge check 44

A student determined the refractive index of glass five times: 1.44, 1.42, 1.46, 1.56, 1.43. What should the student quote as the mean value for refractive index, and why?

Knowledge check 45

Calculate the number of measurements taken in a minute by a data logger that is sampling at 0.5 Hz.

Knowledge check 46

A magnet is dropped from rest through a vertical coil of length 50 mm. Show that it takes about 100 ms for the magnet to pass through the coil.

Worked example

A magnet is dropped through a coil of many turns. This is connected to a voltage sensor, which records the induced e.m.f. as the magnet falls through the coil (Figure 27a). Typical results are shown in Figure 27b.

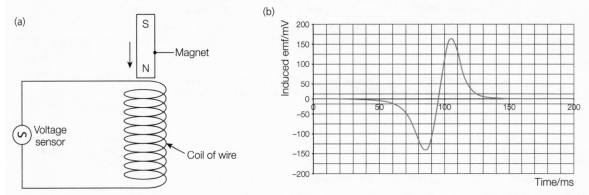

Figure 27

Discuss the advantages of using a data logger to collect these data.

Answer

You should include the following points:

■ The event happens over about 100 ms, which does not give enough time for the data to be recorded manually.
■ The high sample rate of the data logger enables the induced e.m.f. to be measured hundreds of times during this short time interval.
■ This produces enough data for a graph to be plotted showing how the induced e.m.f. varies with time.
■ If the data logger is connected to a computer, the graph can be shown directly.

Recording data

You will be expected to *present observations and data in an appropriate format*. You may also need to *use appropriate mathematical skills to analyse quantitative data*.

Tabulating data

Data must be clearly recorded in a table. Tables should have headings with the quantity and units separated by a forward slash (e.g. current/mA). You should also ensure the number of significant figures, or decimal places, is appropriate, and these should be consistent down each column. The independent variable should normally be the first column of the table.

Table 6 shows how data should be recorded using results from an experiment to measure electrical power.

Table 6 Recording results

Potential difference V/V	Current I/mA
6.01	58.8
4.63	50.8
3.31	41.8
2.16	32.9

Knowledge check 47

What is wrong with this table?

Volts	A
5.85 V	0.05
4.38 V	0.04
2.94 V	0.03
1.4 V	0.01

Content Guidance

Worked example

(A-level only) In an experiment to investigate whether radioactive decay is exponential, a student decides to plot a graph of the natural logarithm of the activity A, which is measured in counts per second, against time t, which is measured in seconds. Draw a table showing the headings that the student should use in order to record these data.

Answer

Time t/s	Activity A/s^{-1}	$\ln(A/\text{s}^{-1})$

Significant figures

When recording data, it is important to *write down* the data to the number of significant figures given by the resolution of the device being used. For digital instruments, you should write down all the numbers shown on the device, e.g. times should be *recorded* to 0.01 s if using a digital stopwatch. Only in the subsequent processing should you round to the appropriate number of significant figures. The following examples show how to correctly use significant figures in recorded and processed data.

Worked example

In an experiment to find the period T of a simple pendulum, the times shown in Table 7 are recorded for 20 oscillations.

Table 7

t_1/s	t_2/s	t_3/s	Mean t/s	T/s	T^2/s^2
14.72	14.65	14.67			

Complete the table by adding values of t, T and T^2.

Answer

$$\text{mean } t = 14.68\,\text{s}$$

$$T = t/20 = 0.734\,\text{s}$$

$$T^2 = 0.539\,\text{s}^2$$

Worked example

The following data were recorded for a trolley accelerating down an inclined plane:

    initial velocity of the trolley = $1.23\,\mathrm{m\,s^{-1}}$

    final velocity of the trolley = $1.97\,\mathrm{m\,s^{-1}}$

    time taken = $1.6\,\mathrm{s}$

Use these data to calculate the acceleration of the trolley, quoting your answer to the appropriate number of significant figures.

Answer

$$a = (v - u)/t = (1.97 - 1.23)\,\mathrm{m\,s^{-1}}/1.6\,\mathrm{s}$$

$$= 0.4625\,\mathrm{m\,s^{-2}} = 0.46\,\mathrm{m\,s^{-2}}$$

(Answer is to 2 s.f. because the time is recorded to only 2 s.f. even though the velocities are recorded to 3 s.f.)

Analysing results

You will be expected to:

- *plot and interpret suitable graphs*
- *process and analyse data*

Working through the *Maths and Units* section of this student guide will give you plenty of practice in developing your mathematical skills. You should note that more advanced mathematical skills are required for A-level than for AS, which mainly means ensuring that you are confident in handling exponential functions and drawing and analysing logarithmic graphs.

Plotting a graph is a key first step in analysing your results. All graphs should be drawn with sensible scales and with appropriately labelled axes, including correct units. Points should be plotted accurately and a thin straight line, or smooth curve, of best fit drawn.

What graph should I draw?

Physicists often carry out experiments in order to find an equation that relates the independent (x) and dependent (y) variables. If the graph obtained is a straight line of gradient m and a y-intercept of c, the relationship can be written in the form of $y = mx + c$.

If the graph is a straight line *passing through the origin* ($c = 0$), then we can say that variable y is directly proportional to variable x ($y = mx$). For example, in an experiment to measure the resistance of a wire, the graph shown in Figure 28 was obtained.

Knowledge check 48

In an experiment to measure the acceleration of a trolley, the acceleration was measured three times using two light gates and a data logger:

Acceleration/$\mathrm{m\,s^{-2}}$		
0.44	0.45	0.47

Calculate the mean acceleration, quoting your answer to the appropriate number of significant figures.

Exam tip

It is important that you learn how to rearrange a formula so that you can get a straight-line graph, and are able to identify the variables and the terms for the gradient and intercept (if there is one).

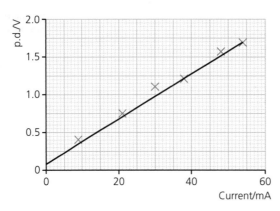

Figure 28

Knowledge check 49

The braking distance of a car is directly proportional to its mass. If a 2000 kg car has a braking distance of 120 m for a particular speed, calculate the braking distance required for a 1400 kg car travelling at the same speed.

The graph does not quite pass through the origin, which is probably due to a systematic error in the measurements. This could be due to a zero error in the ammeter or voltmeter, or possibly some contact resistance at the terminals where the wire is connected into the circuit.

If the line is a straight line but clearly does not pass through the origin, then we can say that there is a *linear relationship* between the two variables, but it is *not* a proportional relationship.

Many experiments result in graphs that are curves. Perhaps there is an inversely proportional relationship between the variables, or a power law? Maybe the relationship is exponential?

Exam tip

You will lose marks if the line is forced through the origin or if a straight line is drawn when the data suggest a curve.

Worked example

Oscillations of a metre rule

The student's teacher in the example on page 36 suggests that a better value for the Young modulus might be obtained if measurements were taken with different masses and a suitable graph was plotted. The relevant equation is

$$E = \frac{16\pi^2 M L^3}{wt^3 T^2}$$

a   For a given metre rule, this equation for the Young modulus contains three variables. State what they are and, following the teacher's suggestion, state which one must be kept constant. How would you ensure this?

b   Explain what should be plotted in order to get a linear graph.

c   Show how the graph could be used, together with the rest of the experimental data, to get a value for the Young modulus.

d   Suggest why a graph is likely to reduce the uncertainty in the value obtained for the Young modulus.

→

Answer

a For a given rule, the three variables are:
  - the suspended mass M
  - the period T
  - the length of suspension L

Of these, L should be kept constant and T should be found for different values of M.

To ensure L remains constant:
  - the masses should be secured tightly
  - the distance should be checked before each timing

b From the equation

$$E = \frac{16\pi^2 M L^3}{wt^3 T^2} \Rightarrow T^2 = \frac{16\pi^2 L^3}{Ewt^3} \times M$$

Therefore, a graph of T^2 against M should be plotted.

c The graph of T^2 against M should be a straight line through the origin:

$$\text{gradient} = \frac{16\pi^2 L^3}{Ewt^3} \Rightarrow E = \frac{16\pi^2 L^3}{\text{gradient} \times wt^3}$$

d Plotting a graph would
  - give an average of a number of readings, and so
  - reduce both random and systematic errors

Exam tip

Practice so that you are confident in arranging complex formulae to give straight-line graphs of the form $y = mx + c$ and in determining which of the terms are variables and which are constant.

Knowledge check 50

How would you check graphically whether the experimental results fit the following equations?

a $mgh = \frac{1}{2}mv^2$ for variables h and v

b $T = 2\pi\sqrt{\dfrac{l}{g}}$ for variables T and l

Lines of best fit

Before you draw a line of best fit, think about the underlying physics to help you decide whether the line should be straight or curved. Perhaps there is a law that applies to these data (e.g. $V = IR$)?

Use these guidelines to ensure that you draw the best possible line of best fit. Examiners expect lines to be drawn carefully (i.e. thin and straight or smooth).

- Try to make sure there are as many points on one side of the line as the other.
- The line should pass very close to the majority of plotted points.
- Are there any obviously anomalous results?
- Are there uncertainties in the measurements? The line of best fit should fall within error bars if these are drawn.
- Use a thin, sharp pencil to draw the line of best fit

Content Guidance

Worked example

How *not* to plot graphs!

Look at the graphs in Figure 29 and decide what is wrong with each one.

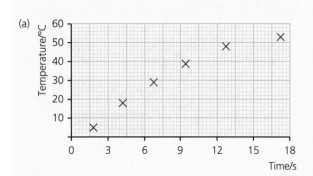

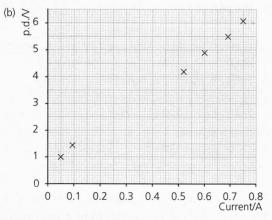

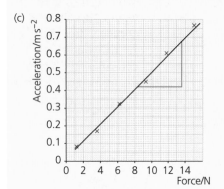

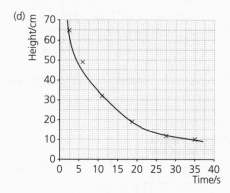

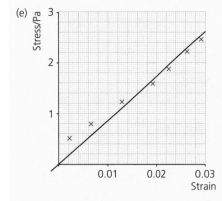

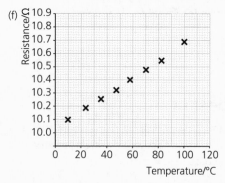

(g)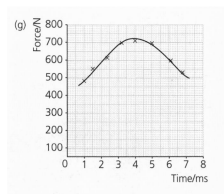

(h)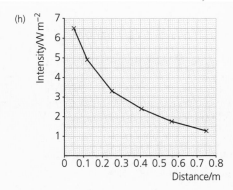

Figure 29

Answer

a Awkward scale divisions — in particular, avoid multiples of 3, because interpolation is difficult.

b No readings between 0.1 A and 0.5 A — a poor distribution of readings makes it difficult to plot a line of best fit.

c The triangle used to calculate the gradient is too small — this would produce large percentage uncertainties in the values of Δx and Δy and therefore in the gradient.

d Poorly drawn curve of best fit — a smooth curve is required (this line is 'spidery').

e The line has been forced through the origin, and so is not the 'best fit'.

f A sharp pencil was not used to plot points, making them very thick — precision is lost.

g Poor y scale — the points do not fill more than half of the y-axis, so the scale could have been doubled.

h A line has been drawn simply joining the points — a *smooth* curve of best fit should have been drawn.

Dealing with anomalous results

You may find that some results do not fit the general pattern and lie a long way from the line of best fit. Circle these and do not include them in your line of best fit. You should make it clear that you have done this. Try to think what may have caused them. Did a different student collect that piece of data? Was a different measuring device used? Did the external conditions change? If there is time, this point should be repeated. You should also exclude any anomalous values when calculating the mean of repeats.

Calculating gradients

A gradient often represents an important quantity, as discussed on page 13 in the section on mathematical requirements.

Exam tip

If you decide to exclude any anomalous result, you should state that you have done so.

Exam tip

You must use a large triangle with a base as large as possible (normally at least 8 cm) and remember to include the units in your final calculation of a gradient.

Worked example

Determining the resistance of a component

The circuit shown in Figure 30 is set up to determine the resistance of a component.

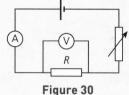

Figure 30

The p.d. (*V*) across the component and the current (*I*) in it were measured for a range of currents, and the results shown in Table 8 were obtained.

a Plot a graph of *V* on the *y*-axis against *I* on the *x*-axis.

b Comment on the graph you obtain.

c Use your graph to determine a value for the resistance of the component.

Table 8

I/μA	V/mV
5.0	1.55
10.0	1.27
15.0	4.98
20.0	6.57
25.0	8.28
30.0	9.87

Answer

a

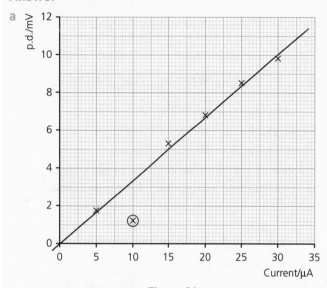

Figure 31

b The graph is a straight line through the origin. The point (10.0 μA, 1.27 mV) is an anomalous result and so is excluded from the line of best fit.

c $R = \dfrac{V}{I} = \text{gradient} = \dfrac{(10.0 - 0.0) \times 10^{-3}}{(30.0 - 0.0) \times 10^{-6}}$

$R = 333\,\Omega = 330\,\Omega$ (2 s.f.)

Knowledge check 52

a State Ohm's law.

b Sketch a graph of the data you would use to check whether a component obeyed Ohm's law.

c How could you tell whether the component was ohmic?

d How could you use your graph to determine the resistance of the component?

Knowledge check 51

What is the resistance of a resistor if the p.d. across it is 4.97 mV when the current in it is 22.6 μA?

Exam tip

When plotting graphs, remember to plot the correct quantities on each axis. Force against time means that force would go on the *y*-axis and time on the *x*-axis.

Worked example

Calculating the spring constant

Explain how you would use the data for the spring constant experiment on pages 33–34 to determine the limit of proportionality and the spring constant.

Answer

- For each extension, calculate the force applied using $W = mg$.
- Plot a graph of force against extension. Note that, contrary to normal practice, we are plotting the dependent variable (extension) on the x-axis. This is so that the gradient gives us the spring constant — see the last bullet point below.
- Read off the point at which the graph begins to curve — the limit of proportionality.
- For the linear region, determine the gradient by drawing a large triangle — this gives the spring constant.

Error bars and uncertainties in the gradient

The uncertainty in a measurement can be shown on a graph as an error bar. If there is an uncertainty in both the quantities y and x, then instead of an error bar you would have an error rectangle.

If you are plotting a log graph, then you have to calculate the logarithm of the maximum and minimum possible values for each data point and determine the error bars using these values.

The uncertainty in each measurement can be determined from the resolution of the data, or it is sometimes quoted as a percentage. Use the following guidelines to help you draw correct error bars:

If there are repeat readings:
- plot the data points at the mean values
- calculate the range of the data, ignoring any anomalies
- add error bars with lengths equal to half the range on either side of the data points
- if you know the absolute uncertainty, plot the error bars based on this straight away

Knowledge check 53

Determine the uncertainty in ln T that should be used to plot error bars if $T = (8.2 ± 0.2)$ N.

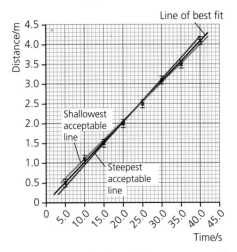

Figure 32

To determine the uncertainty in a gradient, three lines should be drawn on the graph, as shown in Figure 32:

- the line of 'best fit' and
- the steepest (shown in blue) and shallowest (shown in red) gradient lines that can be drawn through the data points (or through the error bars if these are shown)

The gradient of each line should be found. Then:

$$\text{percentage uncertainty in gradient} = \frac{\text{highest (or lowest) possible gradient} - \text{gradient of best fit}}{\text{gradient of line of best fit}} \times 100\%$$

The percentage uncertainty in the y-intercept can be found in a similar way.

Worked example

Investigating a bouncing tennis ball

Two students investigate how high a tennis ball bounces when it is dropped onto a concrete floor (Figure 33).

Figure 33

They drop the ball from different heights h_0 and observe the height h_1 to which it bounces after one bounce. They record their results in a table, as shown in Table 9.

Table 9

h_0/cm	20.0	30.0	40.0	50.0	60.0	70.0
h_1/cm	12.4	17.1	21.4	29.5	32.1	41.5
	10.4	14.9	23.6	27.5	34.9	38.5
Average h_1/cm	11.4	16.0	22.5	28.5	33.5	40.0

The students think that the fraction of energy transferred to the surroundings when the ball bounces may be constant, i.e. mgh_1/mgh_2 is constant.

a Plot a graph of h_1 on the y-axis against h_0 on the x-axis, starting each scale at the origin. Plot your points as error bars for h_1. You may assume that the uncertainty in h_0 is negligible.

b Discuss whether the students' assumption was valid or not.

c Determine the steepest and shallowest gradients and hence a value, with its uncertainty, for the fraction of energy transferred.

➡

d A regulation tennis ball, when dropped from a height of 254 cm onto a concrete surface, must rebound to a height of 135–147 cm. Discuss whether or not the ball in this experiment conforms to this regulation.

e Explain how you would try to reduce the uncertainty of the measurements if you were doing this experiment.

Answer

a Your graph should look like Figure 34. Although you could draw the graph using IT, you must be able to draw such a graph by hand in the exam, so practise both techniques.

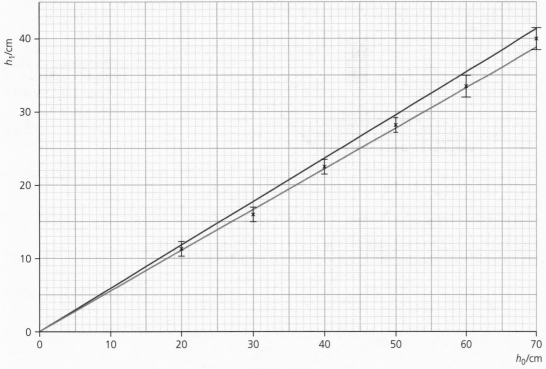

Figure 34

b As the graph is a straight line *through the origin*, $h_1 \propto h_0$, and so the students' assumption would appear to be valid.

c steepest gradient $= \dfrac{(32.5 - 0.0)\,\text{cm}}{(55.0 - 0.0)\,\text{cm}} = 0.59$

shallowest gradient $= \dfrac{(30.5 - 0.0)\,\text{cm}}{(55.0 - 0.0)\,\text{cm}} = 0.55$

best gradient $= 0.57 \pm 0.02$

The fraction of energy transferred to the surroundings is therefore 0.43 ± 0.02 or $43\% \pm 2\%$.

d At 254 cm, rebound height will be $(0.57 \pm 0.02) \times 254\,\text{cm} = 145 \pm 5\,\text{cm}$. As this is within the stated range of 135–147 cm, the ball would appear to conform to the regulation, assuming that the fraction of energy transferred remains the same up to a height of 254 cm.

e Some techniques that would reduce the uncertainty might be to:
- clamp the ruler vertically — checking with a set-square
- use the set-square to check the drop heights
- do a test run at each height so that you can get your eye level with where you expect the bounce to be
- take more than two readings for the bounce height each time

Exponential changes and log graphs

(A-level only) At A-level you will need to be familiar with exponential changes. Common examples include radioactive decay, the decrease in amplitude of a damped oscillator and the discharge of a capacitor through a resistor.

A good example of an exponential relationship is shown in an experiment to investigate how the length of a jelly fibre affects the amount of light that is absorbed (Figure 35). A phototransistor is used to detect the light. This produces a voltage that is directly proportional to the amount of light falling on it.

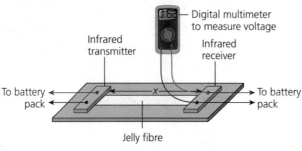

Figure 35

A graph of the data obtained in such an experiment is shown in Figure 36.

The exponential shape of the curve suggests that the intensity of light passing through the fibre might decrease exponentially with length according to the relationship:

$$I = I_0 e^{-\mu x}$$

where I = intensity of light, μ = absorption coefficient of jelly and x = length of jelly.

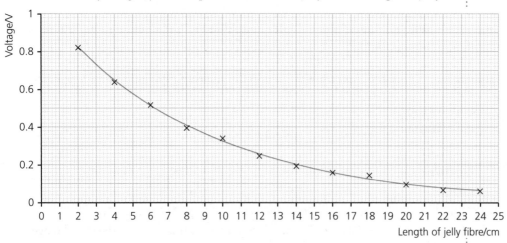

Figure 36

Taking natural logarithms ('ln') on both sides of the equation gives:

$$\ln I = \ln I_0 - \mu x$$

Since the phototransistor voltage V is proportional to the intensity I, we have:

$$\ln V = \ln V_0 - \mu x$$

Comparing with $y = mx + c$, we can see that, if $\ln V$ is plotted on the y-axis against x on the x-axis, we should expect a straight-line graph of gradient $= -\mu$ and y-intercept $= \ln V_0$, as shown in Figure 37. This is called a log-linear graph.

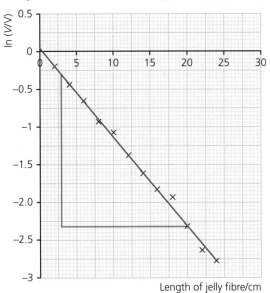

Figure 37

Worked example

a Use the graph in Figure 37 to determine the absorption coefficient, μ.
b Use this graph to find the value of V_0.
c Determine the length of fibre needed to reduce the intensity to 15% of its initial amount.

Answer

a Taking the points (3.00, −0.30) and (20.0, −2.30) gives:

$$\text{gradient} = \frac{-2.30 - (-0.30)}{(20.0 - 3.0)\,\text{cm}} = -0.12\,\text{cm}^{-1}$$

The absorption coefficient is therefore $0.12\,\text{cm}^{-1}$.

b y-intercept $= 0.04 \Rightarrow V_0 = e^{0.04} = 1.0\,\text{V}$

c Substituting $I = 0.15I_0$ and $\mu = 0.12\,\text{cm}^{-1}$ into the equation $I = I_0 e^{-\mu x}$ gives:

$$0.15I_0 = I_0 e^{-0.12x} \Rightarrow \ln(0.15) = -0.12(x/\text{cm}) = -1.897$$

$$(x/\text{cm}) = -1.897/(-0.12)$$

$$x = 16\,\text{cm}$$

Log graphs can also be used to investigate relationships of the form:

$$y = Ax^n$$

where A and n are constants.

Exam tip

You can also test for exponential changes mathematically using the 'constant ratio test'. Applying this to the data shown in Figure 36:

$0.64/0.82 \approx 0.78$

$0.52/0.64 \approx 0.81$

$0.40/0.52 \approx 0.77$

These ratios are all within a few per cent of each other, so within experimental limits we can say that the data show an exponential decrease in voltage with an increase in length.

Exam tip

Always include the units when determining the gradient of a graph.

Exam tip

Always try to check the validity of your answer if possible. Here you should look back at the data and see whether the voltage has dropped to 15% of its original value for a length of 16 cm.

It would take a long time to find n using trial and error, but if we take logs of both sides (either to base '10' or to base 'e') the equation becomes:

$$\log y = \log A + n\log x \qquad \text{or} \qquad \ln y = \ln A + n\ln x$$

A graph of $\ln y$ against $\ln x$ will give a straight line. Comparing this with the equation of a straight line, $y = mx + c$, gives:

$$\ln y = \ln A + n\ln x$$
$$y = \quad c \quad + \quad mx$$

i.e. gradient $m = n$ and intercept $c = \ln A$.

Evaluation

Having taken measurements, analysed the data and presented the data in a suitable format, you can now evaluate your results and draw a conclusion from your data.

Exam questions may ask you to discuss to what extent your results confirm a particular relationship between two variables. You may also be asked to comment on the accuracy and precision of your results, given your analysis of uncertainties. Evaluating the experimental method will allow you to consider how the errors and uncertainties in the experiment could be reduced.

The following worked examples give you practice at applying your knowledge of *planning*, *implementing* and *analysing results* together with *evaluating results* and *drawing conclusions*.

> **Exam tip**
>
> *Reminder*:
>
> The percentage difference between two experimental values is given by:
>
> $$\%\text{difference} = \frac{\text{difference between the values}}{\text{average of the two values}} \times 100\%$$
>
> The percentage difference between an experimental value and a stated or known value is given by:
>
> $$\%\text{difference} = \frac{\text{difference between the values}}{\text{stated value}} \times 100\%$$

> **Knowledge check 55**
>
> a A student determines the spring constant for a spring by two different methods — by measuring the extension for different loads, and by timing vertical oscillations. Values of $26.7\,\text{N}\,\text{m}^{-1}$ and $28.3\,\text{N}\,\text{m}^{-1}$ are obtained, respectively. What is the percentage difference between these two values?
>
> b The student also combines the results of the two experiments to find a value for g of $9.71\,\text{m}\,\text{s}^{-2}$. By what percentage does this value differ from the accepted value for g?

> **Exam tip**
>
> For an exponential function, you *must* use natural logs ('ln').
>
> For investigating a power, you can use either 'ln' or 'log'. If you always use 'ln', you cannot go wrong.

> **Exam tip**
>
> Remember the intercept is $\ln A$ (or $\log A$) and so $A = e^{y\text{-intercept}}$ (or $10^{y\text{-intercept}}$).

Worked example

Investigating resonance

(A-level only) A student plans to investigate how the frequency of vibration of air in a conical flask depends on the volume of air in the flask. He blows directly into the neck of the flask and listens to the sound of the air vibrating. He then pours water into the flask until it is approximately half filled and blows into the flask as before. He notices that the pitch (frequency) of the vibrating air is higher when the flask is half full of water.

He thinks that there might be a relationship between the natural frequency of vibration f of the air in the flask and the volume V of air in the flask of the form $f \propto V^n$, where n is a numerical constant.

The student sets up the arrangement shown in Figure 38.

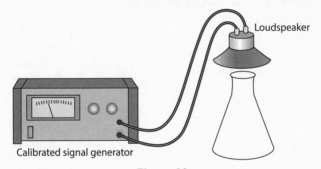

Figure 38

With the flask empty, he increases the frequency of the signal generator until the air in the flask vibrates very loudly. He repeats this for increasing volumes of water in the flask.

a Explain why this happens at the natural frequency of vibration of the air.

b Describe a technique by which the uncertainty in determining this frequency could be reduced.

c Describe how he could vary, and measure, the volume of air in the flask.

d Explain how plotting a graph of $\ln f$ against $\ln V$ would enable him to test whether $f \propto V^n$ and would enable him to find a value for n.

e The student obtained the data given in Table 10.

Table 10

V/cm^3	f_1/Hz	f_2/Hz	f/Hz
554	217	221	219
454	243	241	242
354	271	277	274
254	325	323	324
204	363	359	361
154	412	418	415

Calculate values of $\ln(V/\text{cm})$ and $\ln(f/\text{Hz})$ from the data in the table and add those values to the table. Then plot a graph of $\ln(f/\text{Hz})$ against $\ln(V/\text{cm})$ and use your graph to determine a value for n.

f Explain **qualitatively** whether your value for n is consistent with the student's initial observations or not.

Answer

a When the frequency of the signal generator, i.e. the frequency of vibration of the loudspeaker, is equal to the natural frequency of vibration of the air inside the flask, resonance occurs. Energy is transferred with maximum efficiency from the loudspeaker to the air in the flask, and so this air vibrates very loudly.

b The frequency should be increased gradually until resonance occurs. This frequency should be recorded. The frequency should then be increased beyond the resonant frequency and gradually reduced until once again resonance is detected. This frequency should also be recorded, and the average of the two values should be taken as the resonant frequency.

c A measuring cylinder is required, then:
- this is used to fill the flask to the top with water so that the volume V_f of the flask can be determined
- the flask is then emptied
- a known volume v of water is now added to the flask
- the volume of air will therefore be $V = V_f - v$
- further volumes of water are added to give different volumes V of air in the flask

d The proposed equation is $f \propto V^n$, or $f = kV^n$. If we take logarithms ('ln') on both sides of the equation, we get:

$$\ln f = n \ln V + \ln k$$

So, if a graph of $\ln f$ against $\ln V$ is plotted, this should be a straight line with gradient equal to the constant n and intercept on the y-axis equal to $\ln k$.

e The values are shown in Table 11.

V/cm^3	f/Hz	$\ln(V/\text{cm}^3)$	$\ln(f/\text{Hz})$
554	219	6.32	5.39
454	242	6.12	5.49
354	274	5.87	5.61
254	324	5.54	5.78
204	361	5.32	5.89
154	415	5.04	6.03

→

> **Exam tip**
>
> Note that the technique should be described in detail — an answer such as 'The reading was repeated and the average taken' is not sufficient. This technique can also be applied to focusing an image with a lens.

Your graph should be a straight line of negative slope, as in Figure 39.

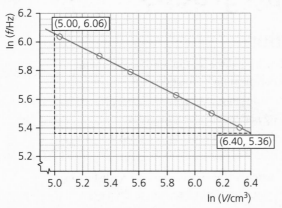

Figure 39

Note that:

- the points should occupy at least half the graph paper in each direction, which means that the scales should *not* start at the origin
- the axes should be labelled exactly as shown: $\ln(f/\text{Hz})$ on the y-axis and $\ln(V/\text{cm})$ on the x-axis
- the points should be plotted to a precision of at least half a square
- a thin, straight line of best fit should then be drawn

The constant n is the gradient of the graph. Taking a large triangle:

$$\text{gradient} = n = \frac{6.06 - 5.36}{5.00 - 6.40} = \frac{+0.70}{-1.40} = -0.50$$

(do not forget the minus sign)

f A negative value of n means that, as the volume of air in the flask gets less, the frequency of vibration (pitch) of the air gets higher, which is consistent with the student's initial observation.

A value of -0.50 suggests that $n = -\frac{1}{2}$, meaning that:

$$f \propto V^{-\frac{1}{2}} \quad \text{or} \quad f \propto \frac{1}{\sqrt{V}}$$

In other words, the frequency of vibration is inversely proportional to the square root of the volume of air.

Knowledge check 56

(A-level only) The period T of vertical oscillations of a mass m on a spring of spring constant k is given by:

$$T = 2\pi\sqrt{\frac{m}{k}}$$

a Write down the expression obtained by taking natural logarithms on both sides of this equation.

b State the value of the gradient when $\ln(T/\text{s})$ is plotted against $\ln(m/\text{kg})$.

c The y-intercept is found to be 0.19. What value does this give for the spring constant k?

■ Practical activity groups

PAG 1 Investigating motion

In this practical activity group (PAG) you may have done a number of experiments to investigate the motion of objects. Typical experiments may include:

- comparing methods of measuring the acceleration due to gravity
- investigating the terminal velocity of falling paper cones or cupcake cases
- investigating the effect of the initial speed of an object on the stopping distance of the object

This PAG gives you the opportunity to use analogue apparatus to measure distances; to use a stopwatch or data logging with light gates for timing; to use methods to increase the accuracy of your measurements; and to use ICT to collect and process data.

Measuring the acceleration due to gravity using a free-falling object

Essential theory

A free-falling object means one that is falling vertically under gravity, with no other forces acting on it. In practice, any object falling in air will experience air resistance. But, provided the object is spherical, made of a dense material and its speed is not excessive, it may be considered to be falling freely. We can then apply the equations of uniformly accelerated motion to the object, in particular:

$$s = ut + \frac{1}{2}at^2$$

If the object is released from rest, $u = 0$. If the object then falls through a height h with acceleration g we get:

$$h = \frac{1}{2}gt^2$$

Rearranging gives us:

$$t^2 = \frac{2}{g} \times h$$

If we plot a graph of t^2 on the y-axis against h on the x-axis, the gradient will be $2/g$.

Planning

There are several ways of doing this experiment: simply dropping a ball from a known height and using a stopwatch to measure the time, using light gates with a data logging interface, strobe photography and video-frame analysis are examples. But in all cases g is calculated from the time taken for a free-falling object to move through a known, measured distance. The main problem is the relatively short times involved.

Knowledge check 57

Show that the time taken for an object to fall 1.2 m under gravity is about 0.5 s.

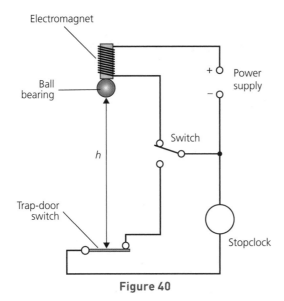

Figure 40

Figure 40 shows one possible method. The points to remember are as follows:

■ The time is measured using an electronic stopwatch that reads to 1/100th of a second.

■ When the switch is in the position shown, the electromagnet is activated and holds the steel ball bearing in place.

■ When the switch is thrown, the electromagnet circuit is broken, releasing the ball, and simultaneously the clock circuit is activated, starting the clock.

■ The clock is stopped when the ball hits the trapdoor and breaks the circuit.

■ The time should be determined at least three times and averaged for each height, over as wide a range of heights as possible.

Safety

The following precautions should be observed:

■ Although low voltages are being used, care should be taken with wiring to prevent any short circuits.

■ A suitable container should be placed under the trapdoor to catch the ball bearing to prevent it from falling on the floor and creating a trip hazard.

Worked example

Table 12 shows a typical set of data. In order to simplify this example, the times indicated are the average of three values for each height. In practice, *all* the values should be shown.

Table 12

h/m	t/s	t²/s²
0.600	0.38	
0.800	0.44	
1.000	0.47	
1.200	0.52	
1.400	0.56	
1.600	0.59	

a Complete Table 12 to show the values of t^2.

b Plot a graph of t^2 against h.

c Determine a value for g from the gradient of your graph.

d Estimate the uncertainty in your value for g, with an explanation of your reasoning.

e Suggest why the graph has a small positive intercept on the t^2 axis.

Answer

a The values of t^2/s^2 are: 0.14, 0.19, 0.22, 0.27, 0.31 and 0.35, respectively.

b Your graph should be like Figure 41.

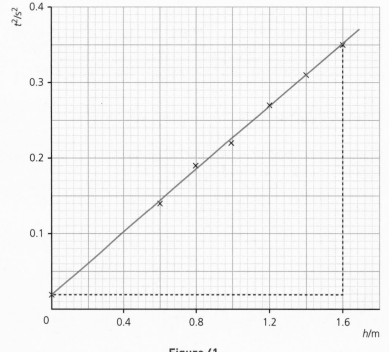

Figure 41

Exam tip

You should always record and show *all* your readings.

Exam tip

You should always draw the line of best fit through the experimental points and not force it through the origin, as there may be a systematic error. One of the reasons for drawing a graph is to identify, and make allowance for, such errors.

c gradient $= \dfrac{(0.35 - 0.02)\,\text{s}^2}{(1.60 - 0.00)\,\text{m}} = 0.20(6)\,\text{s}^2\,\text{m}^{-1} = \dfrac{2}{g}$

This gives $g = \dfrac{2}{0.20(6)\,\text{s}^2\,\text{m}^{-1}} = 9.7\,\text{m s}^{-2}$

d As the values of t could only be measured to 2 s.f., it would be reasonable to state the value for g as $9.7 \pm 0.1\,\text{m s}^{-2}$. Without all the timings, a more detailed analysis is not possible.

e A small positive intercept on the t^2 axis suggests a systematic error, either in t (e.g. a delay in releasing the ball after the switch has been thrown, or a delay in the trapdoor opening after the ball has hit it) or in the measurement of h (all the h values being too small).

> **Exam tip**
>
> Remember to draw a large triangle when determining a gradient and to show the coordinates you have taken in your calculation.

Knowledge check 58

A student uses two light gates to measure free fall due to gravity, as shown in Figure 42. She measures the diameter of the ball. Each light gate times how long the light beam is blocked by the ball, and uses these times to calculate the speed of the ball at A and B. The data logger also records how long it takes the ball to travel between the two light gates.

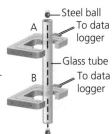

Figure 42

a Suggest why the student has used a glass tube to drop the ball down.

b Explain how the student could calculate g using this method.

PAG 2 Investigating properties of materials

In this practical activity group (PAG) you may have done a number of experiments to investigate the properties of materials. These may include:

- determining the Young modulus for a metal
- investigating the force–extension characteristics for arrangements of springs
- investigating the property of a plastic, such as polyethylene in a carrier bag, or of an elastic band

This PAG gives you the opportunity to use callipers and micrometers to measure small distances; to use metre rules or other apparatus to measure length; and to use digital scales to measure mass.

Determining the Young modulus for a metal

Essential theory

The Young modulus E of a material is defined by the equation:

$$E = \frac{\text{stress}}{\text{strain}} = \frac{F/A}{\Delta l / l} = \frac{Fl}{A\Delta l}$$

Rearranging, we get:

$$F = \frac{EA}{l}\Delta l$$

A graph of the applied force F on the y-axis against the extension Δl on the x-axis will have a gradient EA/l. If we measure the length l, and determine A from a measurement of the diameter d, we can then determine E.

Planning

The extension of even a thin copper wire is only of the order of millimetres, which makes its measurement tricky. Figure 43 shows one example of specialised apparatus used to measure the Young modulus, which incorporates a vernier scale.

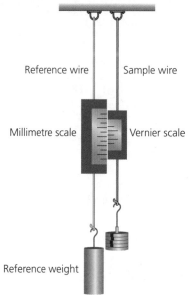

Figure 43

However, a reasonable value can be obtained for the Young modulus by the simple apparatus shown in Figure 44. This has the added advantage that the behaviour of the wire can be investigated up to its breaking point — but see 'Safety' below!

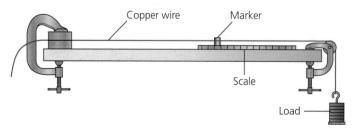

Figure 44

The following procedure should be carried out:
- Thin (e.g. 26 swg or 28 swg) copper wire should be tightly clamped between two wooden blocks to avoid slipping. The wire should be as long as possible — usually about 3 m.

Knowledge check 59

Show that a 3 m length of 28 swg copper wire (diameter 0.376 mm) will extend by about 1 mm when a force of 5 N is applied. The Young modulus of copper is 1.2×10^{11} Pa.

- Weights are added until the wire is just taut and the initial reading of the marker is taken.
- The extension can then be determined for additional loads.

Safety

The following precautions should be observed:
- Place a suitable 'crash pad' under the weights to prevent them hitting the floor directly when the wire breaks.
- Do not put your feet under the weights.
- Wear goggles for protection when the wire breaks.

Worked example

Table 13 shows a set of typical measurements. As the extensions are small, an attempt has been made to record the extensions to a precision of 0.5 mm.

Table 13

Mass added/kg	F/N	Δl/mm	Diameter d/mm
0.50	4.9	1.5	0.38, 0.37, 0.39, 0.38, 0.39, 0.37
1.00	9.8	2.5	Average d = 0.38 ± 0.01 mm
1.50	14.7	3.0	
2.00	19.6	4.0	
2.50	24.5	5.5	**Length l/m**
3.00	29.4	6.0	2.95, 2.93
3.50	34.3	7.5	Average l = 2.94 ± 0.01 m
4.00	39.2	10.0	
5.00	Large extension before wire breaks		

a   Explain how the values for the diameter and the length of wire shown in Table 13 could be determined.

b   Plot a graph of load on the y-axis against extension on the x-axis, using error bars to reflect the precision of ±0.5 mm in the values of extension (although the extension is the dependent variable, it is conventional to plot load against extension or stress against strain).

c   Use the gradient of your graph and the data in the table to determine a value for the Young modulus for copper.

d   Estimate the uncertainty in your value for the Young modulus.

Answer

a   The length can be found using three metre rules (or a 3 m tape measure if available). Even if the precision is only 1 cm, this gives rise to an uncertainty of less than 1%. The length should be measured *from the point where the wire is clamped to the reference point on the marker.*

The diameter should be measured in *different places and at different orientations* along the length of the wire using a digital vernier or micrometer having a precision of 0.01 mm or better.

→

Exam tip

It is good practice to try to interpolate between the scale readings of an instrument if possible, e.g. to 0.5 mm on a millimetre scale or to 0.1°C on a thermometer having graduations of 1°C.

b Your graph should look like Figure 45.

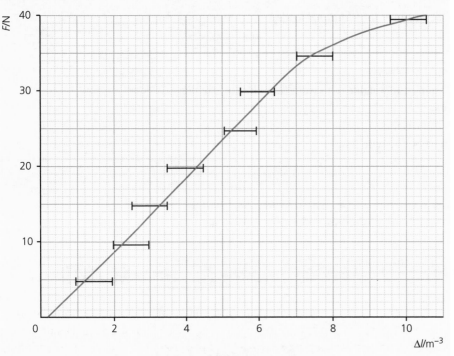

Figure 45

c Determine the gradients for lines of maximum and minimum slope that fall within the error bars. Use the average of these values for your gradient value. This should be approximately $4800 \pm 400\,\mathrm{N\,m^{-1}}$.

$$E = \text{gradient} \times \frac{l}{A} = 4800\,\mathrm{N\,m^{-1}} \times \frac{2.94\,\mathrm{m}}{\pi\left(\frac{1}{2} \times 0.38 \times 10^{-3}\,\mathrm{m}\right)^2}$$

$$= 1.2(4) \times 10^{11}\,\mathrm{Pa}$$

d % uc in diameter $= \dfrac{0.01\,\mathrm{mm}}{0.38\,\mathrm{mm}} \times 100\% = 2.6\%$

% uc in area $A = 2 \times 2.6\% = 5.2\%$

% uc in $l = \dfrac{0.01\,\mathrm{m}}{2.94\,\mathrm{m}} \times 100\% = 0.3\%$

% uc in gradient $= \dfrac{400\,\mathrm{N\,m^{-1}}}{4800\,\mathrm{N\,m^{-1}}} \times 100\% = 8.3\%$

% uc in $E = (5.2 + 0.3 + 8.3)\% = 13.8\%$

Uncertainty in $E = 13.8\%$ of $1.2(4) \times 10^{11}\,\mathrm{Pa} = \pm0.17 \times 10^{11}\,\mathrm{Pa}$

This gives a value for E of $(1.24 \pm 0.17) \times 10^{11}\,\mathrm{Pa}$ or, more realistically, $(1.2 \pm 0.2) \times 10^{11}\,\mathrm{Pa}$

Exam tip

Remember:

- when a quantity is squared, its percentage uncertainty is doubled
- when multiplying quantities, the percentage uncertainty is the sum of the percentage uncertainties of the individual terms
- when dividing quantities, the percentage uncertainty is the sum of the percentage uncertainties of the numerator and denominator

PAG 3 Investigating electrical properties

In this practical activity group (PAG) you may have done a number of experiments to investigate electrical properties. Typical experiments include:

- determining the resistivity of a metal, or the conductivity of an aqueous solution
- investigating electrical characteristics of resistors, lamps and diodes
- determining the internal resistance and maximum power available from a cell

This PAG gives you the opportunity to use digital instruments, including multimeters; to use callipers and micrometers with digital and vernier scales to measure small distances; and to construct circuits from circuit diagrams.

Determining the resistivity or conductivity of a metal

Essential theory

The resistivity ρ of a material is given by the equation:

$$R = \frac{\rho l}{A}$$

where R is the resistance of a length l of the material, having area of cross-section A. The unit for resistivity is $\Omega\,m$.

If we plot a graph of R on the y-axis against l on the x-axis, we should get a straight line through the origin of gradient ρ/A.

If we determine A for the sample, we can then find ρ from $\rho = \text{gradient} \times A$.

The conductivity σ of a material is the inverse of the resistivity:

$$\sigma = \frac{1}{\rho}$$

The unit for conductivity is $\Omega^{-1}\,m^{-1}$.

Planning

The easiest method is to find the resistance of different lengths of resistance wire, such as nichrome, and measure the diameter d of the wire to determine A from $A = \pi d^2/4$.

Note that:

- The resistance of resistance wire is only a few ohms, which makes an ohmmeter unsuitable for measuring the resistance with any degree of precision or accuracy.

- Therefore, an ammeter and a voltmeter must be used and the resistance determined from $R = V/I$.
- The circuit should be set up as shown in Figure 46(a).
- The movable crocodile clip should be pressed firmly on the wire to minimise contact resistance (but not too firmly or the wire will be damaged).

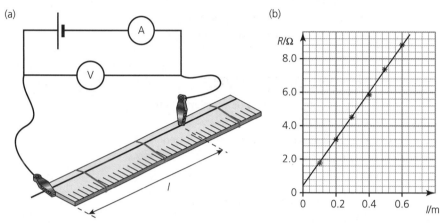

Figure 46

Safety

The following precautions should be observed:

- Although low voltages are being used, care should be taken with wiring to prevent any short circuits.
- See also question **h** in the worked example below.

Worked example

a State what instrument you would use to measure the diameter d of the wire. Justify your choice of instrument.

b The following readings were recorded for the diameter of the wire:
d/mm = 0.31, 0.33, 0.30, 0.39, 0.32
Explain what value you would take for the average diameter.

c Estimate the percentage uncertainty in your value for the diameter of the wire.

d Figure 46(b) shows how the resistance R varies with the length l for such a wire. The intercept on the resistance axis indicates a systematic error. Suggest a possible reason for this.

e Determine the gradient of the graph and hence find a value for the resistivity of nichrome.

f Assuming that the other experimental uncertainties are much less than the uncertainty you calculated in **c**, estimate the uncertainty in your value for the resistivity.

g The cell has an e.m.f. of 1.5 V. Show that the current in the wire is about 0.5 A when a length of 20 cm is connected into the circuit.

h Explain the problem that could arise if short lengths of wire are connected. Suggest any additions that you could make to the circuit to overcome this problem.

→

Knowledge check 63

Show that the resistance of a 50 cm length of 30 swg (diameter 0.3150 mm) nichrome wire is about 7 Ω. The resistivity of nichrome is $1.08 \times 10^{-6}\,\Omega\,m$.

Knowledge check 64

The conductivity of copper is $58.5 \times 10^{6}\,\Omega^{-1}\,m^{-1}$. Calculate the resistivity of copper and use your answer to suggest why copper is used in electrical wiring.

Answer

a A micrometer (or digital vernier) would be suitable because it could measure a diameter of about 0.3 mm with adequate precision (0.01 mm or possibly 0.001 mm, depending on the instrument).

b The 0.39 mm value is likely to be an incorrect reading and so should be ignored when calculating the average. The average is therefore:

$$d = (0.31\,mm + 0.33\,mm + 0.30\,mm + 0.32\,mm) \div 4 = 0.31(5)\,mm$$

c The uncertainty in d should be taken as half the range of values, which is 0.015 mm. The percentage uncertainty in d is therefore:

$$\%\,uc\ in\,d = \frac{0.015\,mm}{0.315\,mm} \times 100\% = 5\%$$

d The intercept indicates a systematic error — a small resistance for zero length of wire. This is probably caused by a poor contact between the crocodile clip and wire at the zero end, giving rise to a small contact resistance. Although there will also be contact resistance between the movable clip and the wire, this will depend on how hard the clip is pressed against the wire, and so is more likely to give rise to random errors.

e gradient $= \dfrac{8.8 - 0.40\,\Omega}{0.6 - 0.00\,m} = 14.0\,\Omega\,m^{-1}$

$A = \pi d^2/4 = [\pi \times (0.315 \times 10^{-3}\,m)^2] \div 4 = 7.7(9) \times 10^{-8}\,m^2$

$\rho = $ gradient $\times A = 14.0\,\Omega\,m^{-1} \times 7.7(9) \times 10^{-8}\,m^2 = 1.09 \times 10^{-6}\,\Omega\,m$

f *Percentage* uncertainty in ρ = percentage uncertainty in A.
As the area is $\pi d^2/4$, the percentage uncertainty in A is $2 \times 5\% = 10\%$.
Uncertainty in $\rho = 10\%$ of $1.09 \times 10^{-6}\,\Omega\,m = 0.109 \times 10^{-6}\,\Omega\,m$.
The value of ρ is therefore best expressed as $(1.09 \pm 0.11) \times 10^{-6}\,\Omega\,m$.
Note that, because there are several values for the diameter, enabling us to get an average with an uncertainty calculated from the spread of readings, we are justified (just) in giving the value for ρ to 3 s.f. With a single reading for the diameter, only 2 s.f. could be justified.

g The resistance of a 20 cm length of wire is $0.2 \times 14.0\,\Omega = 2.80\,\Omega$

$$I = \frac{V}{R} = \frac{1.5\,V}{2.80\,\Omega} = 0.54\,A \approx 0.5\,A$$

h A current of the order of 0.5 A could heat the wire and therefore change its resistivity. This could be overcome by adding a resistor (e.g. 10 Ω) in series with the cell and ammeter.

Exam tip

The diameter of a wire should be measured in different places along the length of the wire and at different orientations to check its uniformity and get a better average value.

Exam tip

Remember that if a quantity is squared then its percentage uncertainty is doubled.

Knowledge check 65

Calculate the diameter of 32 swg gauge nichrome wire that has a resistance per unit length of $18.3\,\Omega\,m^{-1}$.

PAG 4 Investigating electrical circuits

In this practical activity group (PAG) you may have done a number of experiments to build and investigate electrical circuits. Typical experiments include:

- investigating resistance
- investigating circuits with more than one source of e.m.f.
- investigating potential divider circuits that include a non-ohmic device

This PAG gives you the opportunity to use digital instruments, including multimeters; to construct circuits from circuit diagrams, including those where polarity is important (such as diodes); and to construct and check circuits of your own design.

Investigation of potential divider circuits

Essential theory

Simple potential dividers consist of three components in series: a power supply, a fixed resistor and a resistive component whose resistance may be fixed or variable. Figure 47 shows the circuit for a thermistor as resistor R_1.

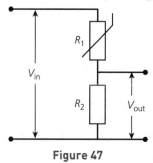

Figure 47

Exam tip

Remember that the resistance of a negative temperature coefficient (NTC) thermistor decreases with increasing temperature.

In this circuit:

$$V_{out} = V_{in} \times \frac{R_2}{R_1 + R_2}$$

If the resistance R_1 of the thermistor decreases as the thermistor warms up, the value of $R_1 + R_2$ will also decrease and so the output voltage V_{out} will increase. This increase in output voltage can be used trigger a switch, and so the circuit can be used as a thermostat.

Other components such as light-dependent resistors (LDRs) and variable resistors can also be used in sensing circuits in a similar way.

Knowledge check 66

Sketch a graph to show how the resistance of an NTC thermistor varies with temperature.

Planning

The experimental arrangement is shown in Figure 48. Points to remember are:

- The value of the resistor should be chosen such that $R_2 \approx R_1$.
- The p.d. across the resistor is measured at 10°C intervals from about 10°C to 60°C.
- The resistance of the thermistor at each temperature can then be calculated using the potential divider formula.
- A graph of output voltage against temperature should be drawn.
- The resistance of the thermistor at any desired temperature within the range investigated can be found by reading off the value of V_{out} from the graph and substituting it into the equation to find R_1.

Knowledge check 67

In Figure 47 V_{in} = 6.0 V and the resistor R_2 has a value of 330 Ω. The manufacturer states that the thermistor R_1 has a resistance of 470 Ω at a temperature of 25°C, with a tolerance of ±2%. Show that the output voltage is about 2.5 V at this temperature.

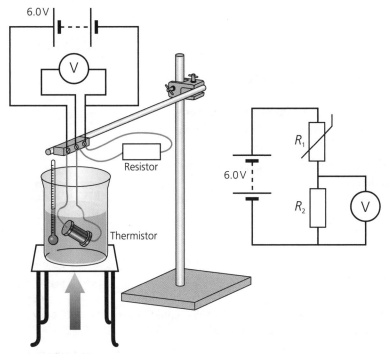

Figure 48

Safety

- Keep the wires well away from the heat source to avoid melting the insulation.
- Make sure the beaker is firmly supported so that it does not topple.
- Use a heat-resistant mat under the heat source.

Worked example

Table 14 shows a typical set of readings.

Table 14

$\theta/°C$	10	20	30	40	50	60
V_{out}/V	1.78	2.25	2.70	3.10	3.44	3.76

a   Describe the techniques you would use to make the readings as accurate as possible and how you would get readings below room temperature.

b   Plot a graph of V_{out} on the y-axis against θ on the x-axis.

c   To what extent is the manufacturer's specification (see Knowledge check 67) confirmed by the experimental data?

d   The output switches an electronic circuit when it reaches 3.00 V. Show that a value for R_2 of about 270 Ω would be needed if the switch is to be used as a thermostat to switch off an immersion heater when the water temperature reaches 45°C.

e   The nearest available preferred value resistor to 270 Ω is 220 Ω. Explain how a switch-off at precisely 45°C could be achieved.

Answer

a To increase the accuracy of readings:
- stir the water continuously
- as you approach the required temperature, turn the heat down and let the temperature stabilise
- keep the thermistor away from the sides and bottom of the beaker

Temperatures below room temperature can be achieved by adding small pieces of ice to the water.

b You should find that your plotted points lie on a gentle curve. You should draw a smooth curve of best fit through them.

c At 25°C the value of $V_{out} = 2.48 \pm 0.02\,V$. Then:

$$V_{out} = V_{in} \times \frac{R_2}{R_1 + R_2} \Rightarrow R_1 = \left(\frac{V_{in} \times R_2}{V_{out}}\right) - R_2$$

so:

$$R_1 = \left(\frac{6.0\,V \times 330\,\Omega}{2.48\,V}\right) - 330\,\Omega = 798\,\Omega - 330\,\Omega = 468\,\Omega$$

If the tolerance in the manufacturer's value of $470\,\Omega$ is $\pm2\%$, the value could be between $461\,\Omega$ and $479\,\Omega$. The experimental value lies within this range, and therefore confirms the manufacturer's specification.

d At 45°C, $V_{out} = 3.28\,V$ so:

$$R_1 = \left(\frac{6.0\,V \times 330\,\Omega}{3.28\,V}\right) - 330\,\Omega = 604\,\Omega - 330\,\Omega = 274\,\Omega$$

To give an output voltage of $3.00\,V$, which is exactly half the input voltage of $6.0\,V$, the value of the resistor must equal the resistance of the thermistor, i.e. $274\,\Omega$.

e This value could be achieved by using a $220\,\Omega$ resistor and adding a small potentiometer (rheostat) in series with it. The thermistor should be immersed in water at 45°C and the potentiometer adjusted until the switch is just activated. The 'thermostat' has then been calibrated to switch off at 45°C.

PAG 5 Investigating waves

In this practical activity group (PAG) you may have done a number of experiments to investigate the properties of different types of waves to identify similarities and differences between their behaviour and characteristics. Typical experiments may include:

- determining the wavelength of light using a diffraction grating or double slits
- determining the speed of sound in air using a resonance tube
- determining the frequency and amplitude of a wave using an oscilloscope

This PAG gives you the opportunity to use analogue apparatus to measure lengths and angles; to use a signal generator and oscilloscope; to generate and measure different types of waves; to use a laser or other light source; and to use ICT to model physical properties.

Exam tip

These are standard techniques applicable to all experiments involving heating a liquid and recording its temperature.

Exam tip

Not all graphs are straight lines. 'Forcing' a straight line through these points would lose marks. You should practice drawing *smooth* curves.

Knowledge check 68

Briefly outline the experimental procedure you could use to investigate the characteristics of an LDR as the variable resistor (R_1) in Figure 47.

Determining the wavelength of light by two-source superposition with a diffraction grating and double slit

Essential theory: diffraction gratings

When monochromatic light, such as a laser beam, is shone through a diffraction grating, a pattern of lines is seen as shown in Figure 49(a). There is a central bright maximum, with further maxima of decreasing intensity on either side. This is represented diagrammatically in Figure 49(b). These effects can be used to determine the wavelength of laser light.

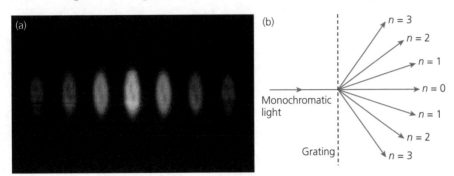

Figure 49

The angle θ of a particular maximum from the central maximum is given by the equation:

$$n\lambda = d \sin \theta$$

where n is the 'order' of the maximum (i.e. $n = 1$ is the first maximum on each side of the central maximum, and so on), d is the separation of the lines of the grating and λ is the wavelength of the light.

Planning

The experimental arrangement is shown in Figure 50. The light source is a laser emitting green light.

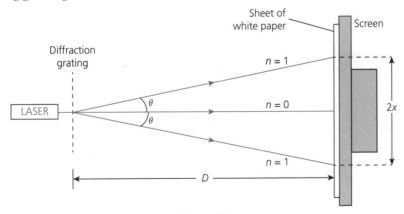

Figure 50

Knowledge check 69

Show that the angle of diffraction of the first order for light of wavelength 550 nm transmitted through a grating of spacing 300 lines per mm is about 10°.

You should proceed as follows:

- Adjust the distance D between the grating and the screen until a number of orders can be seen, sufficiently far apart for their separation to be measured using a millimetre scale.
- Measurements should *not* be attempted directly — the centres of the maxima should be marked on a piece of paper secured to the front of the screen and then processed after the laser has been switched off (see 'Safety' below).
- Measure the distance apart, $2x$, between the maxima of each order and then determine θ for each order using $\tan\theta = x/D$.

Safety

Lasers are potentially **dangerous**! Strict precautions should be observed in their use:

- Never look directly into the beam, or allow anyone else to.
- Never point the beam at anyone.
- Avoid reflections of the beam.
- Always keep your back to the laser when it is on.
- Always switch off the laser when not in use.
- Always work in a well-lit room to prevent the pupils of your eyes dilating.

Worked example

The photograph in Figure 49(a) is *one-quarter* full scale.

a The distance from the grating to the screen was 200 ± 2 mm. Take such measurements as are necessary to determine the angles of diffraction for the first three orders of the green light. Record your measurements in a suitable table.

b The manufacturer states that the grating has a spacing of 300 ± 5 lines per mm. What value does this give for the line separation d?

c Use this, with your values for θ, to find an average value for the wavelength of the green light.

d Estimate the uncertainty in your value for the wavelength.

e Discuss two ways in which you could reduce this uncertainty.

Answer

a Your table should look like this:

Order	2x/mm in photo	2x/mm actual	x/mm	tan θ	θ/°
1	17.0	17.0 × 4 = 68.0	34.0	0.170	9.7
2	34.5	34.5 × 4 = 138.0	69.0	0.345	19.0
3	53.0	53.0 × 4 = 212.0	106.0	0.530	27.9

b Line separation $d = 1/(300 \times 10^3)\,\text{m} = 3.33 \times 10^{-6}\,\text{m}$

Percentage uncertainty in manufacturer's value is $(5/300) \times 100\% = 1.7\%$

Uncertainty in $d = 1.7\%$ of $3.33 \times 10^{-6}\,\text{m} = \pm 0.07 \times 10^{-6}\,\text{m}$

The value for d should therefore be stated as $(3.33 \pm 0.07) \times 10^{-6}\,\text{m}$

c From $n\lambda = d\sin\theta$ we obtain $\lambda = \dfrac{d\sin\theta}{n}$

→

Exam tip

You should always try to make measurements that are as large as possible to minimise experimental uncertainty.

Exam tip

You must be able to both draw and use scaled diagrams.

Exam tip

For a question like e, which asks you to *discuss*, you must both state what you would do *and* explain how this would reduce the uncertainty.

Exam tip

Try to interpolate between scale divisions, e.g. to 0.5 mm on a millimetre scale, as here.

$$n = 1: \ \lambda = \frac{3.33 \times 10^{-6} \, \text{m} \times \sin 9.7°}{1} = 564 \, \text{nm}$$

$$n = 2: \ \lambda = \frac{3.33 \times 10^{-6} \, \text{m} \times \sin 19.0°}{2} = 544 \, \text{nm}$$

$$n = 3: \ \lambda = \frac{3.33 \times 10^{-6} \, \text{m} \times \sin 27.9°}{3} = 520 \, \text{nm}$$

Average $\lambda = 543 \, \text{nm}$

d The range of values is $(564 - 520) \, \text{nm}$ so:

random uncertainty (from measurement of x) = ½ × range = ±22 nm

% random uc = $(22 \, \text{nm}/543 \, \text{nm}) \times 100\% = 4.0\%$

% systematic uc in d = 1.7% (see **b**)

% systematic uc in screen distance = $(2 \, \text{mm}/200 \, \text{mm}) \times 100\% = 1.0\%$

% uc in λ = 4.0% + 1.7% + 1.0% = 6.7%

Uncertainty in λ = 6.7% × 543 nm = 36 nm

We can therefore say that $\lambda = 543 \pm 36 \, \text{nm}$

e The uncertainty could be reduced by:
- moving the screen further away (provided the pattern remains visible) so that the distance between the maxima is greater
- using a grating with smaller line separation, e.g. 600 lines per mm, so that the maxima are further apart

Essential theory: Young's double-slit experiment

Waves from two sources can overlap and undergo superposition. If the two sources of the waves are coherent, then a stable pattern will be produced. This can be demonstrated with sound waves and light waves.

For sound waves, if a single sustained note from a signal generator is played through two identical loudspeakers, an interference pattern of loud and quiet areas is produced, as shown in Figure 51. The point equidistant between the two speakers will have the loudest sound.

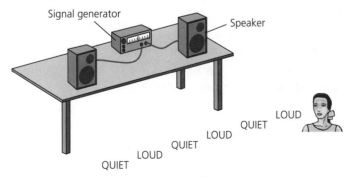

Signal generator

Speaker

LOUD
QUIET
LOUD
QUIET
LOUD
QUIET
LOUD
QUIET

Figure 51

For light waves, when monochromatic light, such as a laser beam, is shone through a double slit, a pattern of lines is seen as shown in Figure 52. There is a central bright maximum, with further maxima of decreasing intensity on either side. These are called Young's fringes.

Knowledge check 70

Assume that the diffraction grating and screen distance in the worked example are kept the same.

a Explain the difference you would observe in the distances between the maxima if the green laser was replaced by a red laser emitting a wavelength of 693 nm.

b (A-level only) Determine how many orders can be observed with this red laser.

Exam tip

Two waves are coherent if they have the same wavelength and there is a constant phase relationship between the two waves.

Knowledge check 71

a Explain why double slits emit light that is coherent.

b Calculate the wavelength of the light being used if the two slits are 0.50 mm apart, the distance to the screen is measured to be 0.80 m and the fringe spacing is 1.0 mm.

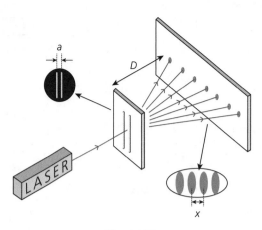

Figure 52

By measuring the slit spacing a, the fringe spacing x and the slits–screen distance D, the wavelength of the light used can be calculated from:

$$x = \frac{\lambda D}{a}$$

Worked example

Students used a red laser to illuminate a double slit with slit spacing = 0.25 mm. They measured the fringe spacing and calculated the wavelength for six different slits–screen distances, as shown in Table 15.

Table 15

D/m	3.00	2.50	2.00	1.50	1.25	1.00
x/mm	7.5	6.3	5.1	3.8	3.1	2.4
λ/nm	625	630	638	633	620	600

a Describe how they should try to determine the fringe spacing accurately.

b Calculate the mean value for the wavelength, together with the uncertainty in this value.

c The manufacturer states the wavelength of the laser to be 630 nm. Discuss whether or not the students' results are consistent with this value.

d The students' teacher suggests that the wavelength could be found by means of a graph. What graph should be plotted, and how could the wavelength be found from the graph?

e Explain what would be seen if a green laser was used to illuminate the double slits.

Answer

a The students should measure across several fringes. The fringe spacing x can then be obtained by dividing this measurement by the number of fringes. It is sometimes easier to take measurements from the centres of the dark fringes, because the centres of the bright fringes may be more difficult to locate than the centres of the dark fringes.

b Mean wavelength = (625 + 630 + 638 + 633 + 620 + 600) nm/6 = 624 nm

The uncertainty can be estimated by calculating half the range:

½ × (638 nm − 600 nm) = 19 nm ⇒ wavelength = 624 ± 19 nm

→

c As the stated value of 630 nm falls within this range, the students' value is consistent with the manufacturer's value, allowing for the uncertainty of the experiment.

d From the formula $x = \dfrac{\lambda D}{a}$, we can see that a graph of x against D should be plotted. Then the gradient will be $\lambda/a \Rightarrow \lambda = \text{gradient} \times a$.

e The fringe spacing is directly proportional to the wavelength of the light used. As green light has a shorter wavelength, the green fringes would be closer together.

PAG 6 Investigating quantum effects

In this practical activity group (PAG) you may have done a number of experiments to investigate the properties of electromagnetic radiation. Typical experiments may include:

■ determining the Planck constant using coloured light-emitting diodes (LEDs)
■ investigating refraction of light using different media, and using lenses
■ observing the effects of polarisation on light and microwaves

This PAG gives you the opportunity to use digital instruments, including multimeters; to construct circuits from circuit diagrams; to use a laser or other light sources to investigate characteristics of light; and to use methods to increase the accuracy of measurements.

Determining the Planck constant using LEDs

Essential theory

Quantum theory treats electromagnetic radiation as photons. The energy, E, of photons is given by the equation:

$$E = hf \ or \ E = \frac{hc}{\lambda}$$

where h is the Planck constant (6.63×10^{-34} J s), f is the frequency of the light, c is the speed of light and λ is the wavelength of the light.

LEDs make use of the movement of electrons between two semiconductor materials to produce photons of light. Each different colour of LED will have a minimum value of p.d., V, that will allow the diode to conduct. The energy of each photon will be equal to the energy gained by an electron, eV:

$$eV = \frac{hc}{\lambda} \Rightarrow V = \frac{hc}{e} \times \frac{1}{\lambda}$$

If we plot a graph of V on the y-axis against $1/\lambda$ on the x-axis, we should get a straight-line through the origin of gradient hc/e.

Planning

One experimental set-up for measuring the Planck constant is shown in Figure 53. At least five different LEDs of known wavelength should be used. The following procedure should be carried out:

■ Place a black cardboard tube over the first LED to reduce ambient light.
■ Look down the tube at the LED.

> **Knowledge check 72**
>
> Show that the energy of a photon of light with a frequency of 5.60×10^{13} Hz is about 4×10^{-20} J.

- Starting from 0 V, slowly increase the voltage until the LED *just* emits light. Write down the potential difference across the LED at this point. Repeat this measurement two more times to get an average value.
- Repeat using the other four coloured LEDs.
- If LEDs with current-limiting resistors (see 'Safety') are used, ensure that the p.d. is measured across the LED only by making connections with crocodile clips onto the legs of the LED.

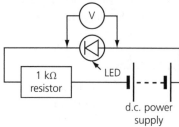

Figure 53

Knowledge check 73

Calculate the energy gained by an electron when a potential difference of 2.5 V is applied to an LED.

Safety

The following precautions should be observed:

- Very bright LEDs (especially blue ones) can dazzle and may cause discomfort. Do not stare for long periods of time at any of the LEDs during the experiment.
- It is easy to damage the LEDs if the current is too large. Use a resistor in series with the LED, as shown in Figure 53, to reduce this risk.

Worked example

A typical set of results is shown in Table 16.

Table 16

LED colour	Wavelength/nm	Potential difference/V		
Red	633	1.24	1.28	1.25
Orange	615	1.39	1.39	1.38
Yellow	585	1.41	1.42	1.42
Green	525	1.75	1.74	1.76
Blue	470	2.05	2.02	2.06

a The human eye is not very good at detecting light at the extremes of the visible spectrum. Describe what effect this might have on the values of p.d. obtained.
b Suggest how this effect could be minimised.
c Calculate the mean value of p.d. for each LED.
d Plot a graph of V against $1/\lambda$.
e Determine a value for the Planck constant using the gradient of your graph.
f By drawing the steepest and shallowest lines of best fit, determine the percentage uncertainty in your gradient and hence the percentage uncertainty in your value for the Planck constant.
g The accepted value for the Planck constant is 6.63×10^{-34} J s. Calculate the percentage difference between your value and the accepted value. Comment on this difference.

→

Answer

a The p.d. values for the red and blue LEDs may be higher than the minimum value at which photons are actually emitted.

b Making observations in a darkened room, and using a cardboard tube on top of the LED, will help to cut out ambient light and make the LED more visible.
Alternatively, an ammeter could be used to find the value of p.d. at which a charge just begins to flow through the LED. This will remove the need to view the emitted light.

c Red, 1.26 V; orange, 1.39 V; yellow, 1.42 V; green, 1.75 V; blue 2.04 V

d Your graph should look like Figure 54.

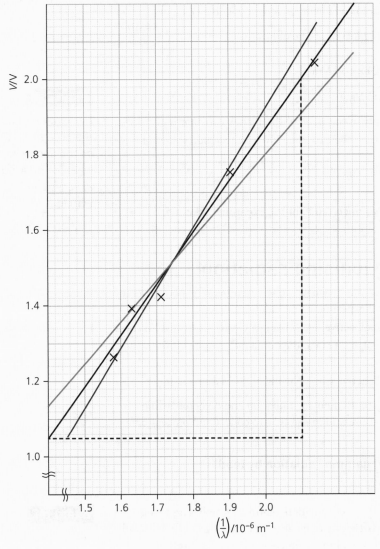

Figure 54

→

Exam tip

It is good practice *not* to include the origin if you have not measured that value — this would give rise to a small scale for the graph, as would be the case here.

e $\text{gradient} = \dfrac{(2.00 - 1.05)\,\text{V}}{(2.10 - 1.40) \times 10^6\,\text{m}^{-1}} = 1.36 \times 10^{-6}\,\text{V m}$

$\text{gradient} = \dfrac{hc}{e} \Rightarrow h = \dfrac{e \times \text{gradient}}{c}$

$\Rightarrow h = \dfrac{1.60 \times 10^{-19}\,\text{C} \times 1.36 \times 10^{-6}\,\text{V m}}{3.00 \times 10^8\,\text{m s}^{-1}} = 7.25 \times 10^{-34}\,\text{J s}$

f Show for yourself that the steepest gradient (blue in Figure 54) is about $1.60 \times 10^{-6}\,\text{V m}$ and the shallowest gradient (red) is about $1.12 \times 10^{-6}\,\text{V m}$. Then:

$$\begin{aligned}\text{\% uncertainty} \atop \text{in gradient}\end{aligned} = \dfrac{\tfrac{1}{2} \times (\text{highest possible gradient} \; - \; \text{lowest possible gradient})}{\text{gradient of line of best fit}} \times 100\%$$

$$= \dfrac{\tfrac{1}{2} \times (1.60 - 1.12) \times 10^{-6}\,\text{V m}}{1.36 \times 10^{-6}\,\text{V m}} \times 100\% = 18\%$$

Hence the percentage uncertainty in the value of the Planck constant is also 18%.

g The percentage difference between the experimental and accepted values of h is:

$$\dfrac{(7.25 - 6.63) \times 10^{-34}}{6.63 \times 10^{-34}} \times 100\% = 9\%$$

This difference is within the 18% uncertainty of the experimental value.

> **Exam tip**
>
> Make sure that you use the correct value for wavelength in your calculation of gradient. It should be converted into metres to allow calculation of the Planck constant.

> **Exam tip**
>
> Remember to use the accepted value as the denominator when comparing an experimental value with it.

PAG 7 Investigating ionising radiation

In this practical activity group (PAG) you may have done a number of experiments to investigate ionising radiation. Typical experiments include:

- observing the random nature of radioactive decay using a Geiger–Müller (GM) tube
- investigation of the absorption of alpha, beta and gamma radiation by differing materials
- determining the half-life of a radioactive isotope using an ionisation chamber

This PAG gives you the opportunity to use ionising radiation and detectors while following a standard operating procedure and to use ICT to collect and process data.

Investigating the absorption of gamma radiation by lead

Essential theory

You should know that, of the three types of radiation, gamma (γ) radiation is the most penetrating. While alpha (α) particles can be absorbed by a sheet of paper and beta (β) particles by a few millimetres of aluminium, γ-rays are not entirely absorbed even by several centimetres of lead. Because the absorption of γ-rays is governed by probability — either the photon of γ radiation is absorbed by an atom of the material

> **Exam tip**
>
> Remember that radioactive emission is a *random* process.

or it is not — the probability of absorption is proportional to the thickness x. This gives an exponential absorption of the form:

$$A = A_0 e^{-\mu x}$$

where A is the activity, or count rate, and μ is a constant — a property of the absorbing material called its absorption coefficient.

Planning

The apparatus is set up as shown in Figure 55. Initially the cobalt-60 source should not be in the laboratory.

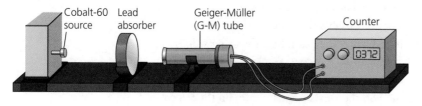

Figure 55

The procedure is then as follows:

■ Measure the thickness of each of the lead absorbers.
■ Determine the background count.
■ Put the cobalt-60 source in place.
■ Record the count rate for different thicknesses x of absorber.
■ Subtract the background count rate to get the corrected count rate A.

A similar procedure can be followed for α and β radiation, using paper or aluminium foil, respectively, as the absorbing material.

Safety

Danger: radiation can cause unseen damage. The following safety precautions *must always be adopted* when using radioactive sources.

■ Keep sources in their lead storage containers when not in use and use only one source at a time in any one investigation.
■ Limit the time of exposure of sources — return to secure storage as soon as possible.
■ Keep your body a sensible distance from the source (at least 30 cm) and ensure that the source is pointed away from yourself and other people.
■ Use a tool to handle sealed sources — this should keep your hands at least 10 cm from the source.
■ Do not eat, drink or apply cosmetics while working with a radioactive source.
■ Wash your hands after working with a radioactive source.

Your teacher will also take other precautions related to the secure storage and documentation for radioactive sources. The sources will be signed out of storage and will not be left unattended by a member of staff, unless the sources are locked into a temporary store.

Knowledge check 74

Sketch a graph representing the expression $A = A_0 e^{-\mu x}$.

Exam tip

You should be aware of the dangers of radiation and must learn the essential safety precautions.

Worked example

Table 17 shows a typical set of data. The count rate has been corrected for background radiation. Four lead discs of different thickness were used.

Table 17

x/mm	0.0	1.7	3.4	5.1	6.8	8.5	10.2	11.9	13.6	15.3	17.0
A/min^{-1}	405	365	340	290	270	250	217	201	189	158	150
ln (A/min^{-1})	6.00	5.90									

a Describe how you would determine the background count rate.

b In this experiment, what is the control variable that must be kept constant?

c Deduce the thicknesses of the four discs and explain how the other values of x are obtained. Illustrate your answer with reference to $x = 13.6$ mm.

d How would you measure the thicknesses of the four discs?

e Explain why a graph of ln (A/min^{-1}) on the y-axis against x/mm on the x-axis should be a straight line.

f Complete the table to show the remaining values of ln (A/min^{-1}) and then plot a graph of ln (A/min^{-1}) on the y-axis against x/mm on the x-axis.

g Use your graph to determine a value for the absorption coefficient μ.

h Suggest why there is considerable scatter in the values, particularly for larger thicknesses of absorber.

Answer

a The background count should be recorded for at least 5 minutes without the source present and then repeated and averaged.

b The control variable is the distance between the source and the detector.

c The thicknesses of the four discs must be the first four values of x/mm: 1.7, 3.4, 5.1 and 6.8.

The other values of x are obtained by using two or more discs in combination. For example, for 13.6 mm, a combination of the 1.7 mm + 5.1 mm + 6.8 mm discs would be used.

d The thickness of each disc should be found using either vernier callipers or a micrometer. After checking for zero error, at least three readings for each disc should be taken and averaged.

e By taking logs to base 'e' ('ln') of both sides of the equation $A = A_0 e^{-\mu x}$, we get:

$$\ln A = \ln A_0 - \mu x$$

or, rearranging:

$$\ln A = -\mu x + \ln A_0$$

So a graph of ln (A/min^{-1}) against x/mm should be a straight line of gradient $-\mu$ and intercept ln (A_0/min^{-1}).

Exam tip

You need to be confident in obtaining a linear graph of an exponential expression by taking natural logarithms (i.e. 'ln' to base 'e').

f The remaining values of ln (A/min^{-1}) are 5.83, 5.67, 5.60, 5.52, 5.38, 5.30, 5.24, 5.06 and 5.01. Your graph should look like Figure 56.

g From the points (17.2, 5.00) and (0.0, 6.00):

$$\text{gradient} = \frac{5.00 - 6.00}{(17.2 - 0.0)\,\text{mm}}$$

$$= 0.058\,\text{mm}^{-1} = -\mu$$

If you draw lines of maximum and minimum slope, you will find that the uncertainty in the gradient is about 0.002, giving a value for μ of $0.058 \pm 0.002\,\text{mm}^{-1}$.

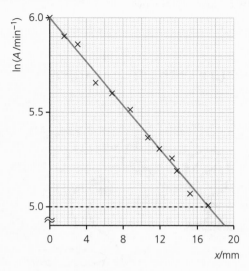

Figure 56

h The scatter is most likely to be due to the random nature of radioactivity. With larger thicknesses, the count rate is smaller and so the random effect is more apparent.

Exam tip

Note that, because the origin has no particular significance, the y-scale of the graph starts at 5.0 to give a large scale. This is often the case when plotting log graphs. Here, a graph that included the origin would be penalised.

Knowledge check 75

As an exercise, draw a graph of A against x. Explain how you could quickly check whether your graph was an exponential curve or not.

PAG 8 Investigating gases

In this practical activity group (PAG) you may have done a number of experiments to investigate the properties of gases. Typical experiments may include:

- estimating a value for absolute zero from gas pressure and volume
- investigating the relationship between pressure and volume
- estimating the work done by a gas as its temperature increases

This PAG gives you the opportunity to use analogue apparatus to measure pressure, volume and temperature, and to interpolate between scale markings.

Estimating a value for absolute zero using variation of gas temperature with pressure or volume

Essential theory

The gas laws are closely linked and you should be familiar with them all.

- **Temperature–pressure law**: the pressure of a *fixed mass* of gas is proportional to its absolute temperature *provided that the volume is kept constant*.

  We can express the temperature–pressure law mathematically by:

  $$p \propto T \Rightarrow \frac{p}{T} = \text{constant}$$

- **Charles' law**: the volume of a *fixed mass* of gas is directly proportional to its absolute temperature *provided that the pressure is kept constant*.

Exam tip

When asked to state the gas laws, you must always give the necessary conditions, e.g. for the temperature–pressure law: a fixed mass, and at a constant volume. If not, you will lose marks.

Knowledge check 76

A closed gas syringe contains a fixed mass of air at 21°C. The syringe is heated until the volume of gas has doubled. If the pressure remains constant, show that the new temperature of the syringe is 315°C.

We can express Charles' law mathematically by:

$$V \propto T \Rightarrow \frac{V}{T} = \text{constant}$$

Variation of gas pressure with temperature

Planning

Two possible ways of doing the experiment are shown in Figure 57.

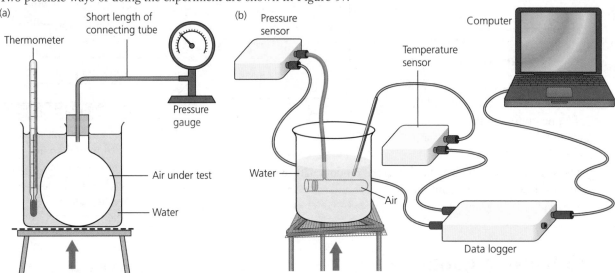

Figure 57

In Figure 57 the tubes connecting the container of gas with the pressure gauge (a) or pressure sensor (b) are kept as short as possible because they contain gas which is not at the same temperature as the main volume of gas. The procedure is as follows:

- Fill the beaker with ice (or ice and salt) to obtain as low a temperature as possible.
- Record the temperature θ and corresponding pressure p of the air in the flask.
- Allow time for thermal equilibrium to be reached between readings — stir the water regularly and turn down the heat while waiting for the air in the flask to reach the temperature of the water.
- Take measurements at regular intervals up to the boiling point of water.

Safety

- It is important to avoid excessive pressure and to ensure that connections are secure.
- The flask chosen as the pressure vessel much be able to withstand the increase in pressure.
- Wear eye protection during the experiment.
- The apparatus should be checked by a teacher or technician before use.

> **Exam tip**
>
> Remember that $T/K \approx \theta/°C + 273$.

> **Exam tip**
>
> If you describe the method of data logging similar to that shown in Figure 57(b), you need to draw all the apparatus and state that you would select 'x-axis = temperature' and 'y-axis = pressure' from the graph menu. 'Use a computer' is not detailed enough.

Worked example

Table 18 shows a typical set of data.

Table 18

T/°C	−5	0	20	40	60	80	100
p/kPa	88	93	100	107	114	121	128

a State the independent, dependent and control variables in this experiment.

b Explain how the necessary conditions for the temperature–pressure law are ensured.

c Plot a graph of p on the y-axis and T on the x-axis. You may find it helpful to use ICT to plot your graph.

d Use your graph to obtain an estimate for the value of absolute zero.

e Identify two main sources of uncertainty in obtaining your value for absolute zero.

Answer

a If you change the temperature and then measure the subsequent change in pressure, the independent variable is the temperature and the dependent variable is the pressure. The control variables are the mass and volume of the air.

b To ensure the necessary conditions:
- the air in the tube or syringe must not be able to leak out, so that its mass will remain constant
- the containers should have rigid walls, so that the volume does not increase as the pressure does

c If you are using ICT to plot the data, then your graph will look like that in Figure 58. A linear trend line has been fitted, which gives the equation of the line as:

$$y = 0.3708x + 91.23$$

Note that the ICT has automatically put in the origin. This does not matter if ICT is being used to determine the equation of the line, but if the graph is drawn by hand the origin should not be included. This would give a larger scale for the graph and improve accuracy in determining the gradient and intercept.

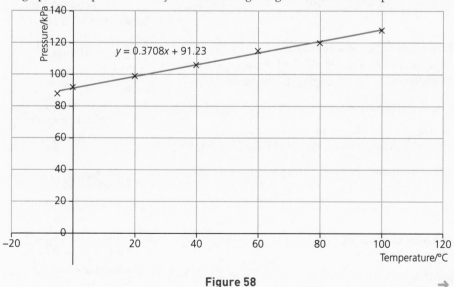

Figure 58

d Using ICT to estimate absolute zero we need to use the trend line to calculate the value of x for which $y = 0$ in the equation:

$$y = 0.3708x + 91.23$$

When $y = 0$ we can write:

$$0 = 0.3708x + 91.23 \Rightarrow x = \frac{-91.23}{0.3708} = -246°C$$

If you plot the graph by hand, then you could choose a suitable scale for the x-axis that allows extrapolation back to $y = 0$, or substitute coordinates from the graph into $y = mx + c$ and solve to find c.

e There are two main sources of uncertainty in this experiment:
  - Only a small range of temperatures on the Kelvin scale are realistically obtainable.
  - You need to extrapolate back a long way to obtain the value for absolute zero. Small changes in the gradient of the line of best fit can therefore lead to relatively large changes in the value for absolute zero.

PAG 9 Investigating capacitors

In this practical activity group (PAG) you may have done a number of experiments to investigate capacitors. Typical experiments include:
- investigating the charging and discharging of capacitors
- investigating capacitors in series and parallel
- investigating the factors affecting the capacitance of a capacitor

This PAG gives you the opportunity to use digital instruments (including multimeters) to measure current, voltage, resistance and time; to design, construct and check circuits; and to use ICT to collect, model and process data.

Determining the time constant using a log graph

Essential theory

You should be familiar with the formula for a capacitor of capacitance C being discharged through a resistor of resistance R. The potential difference (p.d.) V across the capacitor decreases exponentially with time t according to the equation:

$$V = V_0 e^{-t/RC}$$

where V_0 is the p.d. when $t = 0$. The product RC is called the time constant for the discharge. This is the time for the p.d. to fall to $1/e$ of its initial value, i.e. $0.368V_0$.

We need to rearrange the equation for V into the form $y = mx + c$. First we get:

$$\frac{V}{V_0} = e^{-t/RC}$$

Then taking natural logs of both sides gives:

$$\ln\left(\frac{V}{V_0}\right) = -\frac{t}{RC}$$

> **Knowledge check 77**
>
> Sketch a graph of p against T in kelvin, and explain how the graph would show that the two quantities are directly proportional.

> **Knowledge check 78**
>
> a Show that the time constant for a $220\,\mu F$ capacitor discharging through a $3.3\,k\Omega$ resistor is of the order of 1 s.
> b Use the exponential equation to explain why RC must have the unit of seconds.
> c Confirm this by considering the units of resistance and capacitance.

> **Exam tip**
>
> Remember that the product RC gives an order of magnitude for the timescale for the discharge of a capacitor.

Recalling that $\ln(a/b) = \ln a - \ln b$, we can rewrite our equation to separate the dependent variable:

$$\ln(V) - \ln(V_0) = -\frac{t}{RC} \Rightarrow \ln(V) = -\frac{t}{RC} + \ln(V_0)$$

Plotting a graph of $\ln V$ on the y-axis against t on the x-axis, the gradient will be $-1/RC$ and the intercept on the y-axis will be equal to $\ln V_0$.

Planning

As capacitors normally have values of the order of microfarads (μF), the time constant will be short unless the resistance is very large — see Knowledge check 78. Using a data logger and computer allows charge and discharge curves to be obtained even for very short time constants.

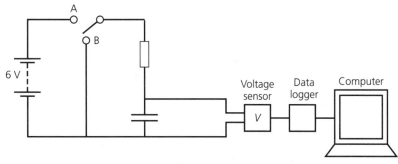

Figure 59

The experimental arrangement is shown in Figure 59. Points to remember are:
- The capacitor is charged through the resistor by connecting the switch to contact A and then discharged through the same resistor by moving the switch to contact B.
- The p.d. across the capacitor is measured by the voltage sensor and recorded by the data logger.
- The data can then be analysed using the computer.

Safety

- **Danger!** If an electrolytic capacitor is being used, its polarity *must* be observed, i.e. the end marked positive (+) *must* be connected to the positive side of the power supply.
- Do not use an a.c. power supply.
- Even though the p.d. is low, care should be taken to avoid any short circuits.
- Check that the value of the p.d. is compatible with the voltage sensor and the capacitor.

Worked example

A student charges a capacitor of unknown value to $6.00\,V$ and then discharges it through a nominal $330\,k\Omega$ resistor.

The data logger was set to take readings of potential difference (V) every $0.5\,s$ for $40\,s$ during discharge. However, for ease of calculation, the data reproduced in Table 19 show only a selection of the values obtained.

Exam tip

You must be able to convert a logarithmic/ exponential equation into a linear form by taking natural logarithms on both sides of the equation.

Exam tip

Remember that the values stamped on resistors and capacitors are what are called 'nominal values' and are subject to a manufacturing tolerance. This is usually 1% or 2% for resistors and can be as much as 10% or even 20% for capacitors.

Table 19

t/s	0.00	1.00	2.00	4.00	8.00	12.00	16.00	20.00	25.00	30.00	40.00
V/V	6.00	5.14	4.46	3.25	1.74	0.98	0.52	0.28	0.13	0.05	0.01
ln(V/V)											

a Complete the table by calculating the values of $\ln(V/V)$.

b Plot a graph of $\ln(V/V)$ against t.

c Determine a value for the time constant, RC, of the circuit from the gradient of your graph.

d The value of the resistor is checked with a digital multimeter using the ohmmeter setting and is found to be $334\,\text{k}\Omega$. The manufacturer's tolerance is given as $\pm2\%$ for the resistor. Discuss whether the measured value of resistance is within tolerance or not.

e Use the measured value of resistance to calculate the capacitance of the capacitor in the circuit. Give your answer to a suitable number of significant figures.

f The student's teacher suggests that the capacitor could have a nominal value of $22\,\mu\text{F}$, which is a 'preferred' value. Discuss whether or not this could be the case.

Answer

a You should obtain the following values:

V/V	6.00	5.14	4.46	3.25	1.74	0.98	0.52	0.28	0.13	0.05	0.01
ln(V/V)	1.79	1.64	1.50	1.18	0.55	−0.02	−0.65	−1.27	−2.04	−3.00	−4.61

b Your graph should look similar to that shown in Figure 60.

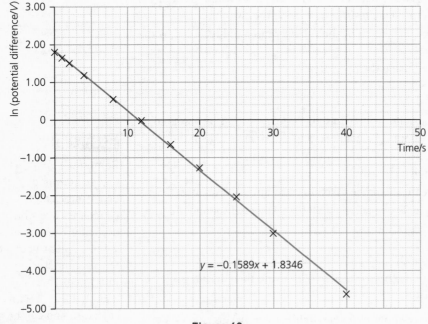

Figure 60

c If you plot the data by hand, then you would calculate the gradient using a large triangle drawn on the graph. A spreadsheet program provides a linear trend line for the data as shown in Figure 60.

$$y = -0.1589x + 1.8346$$

The gradient is therefore = −0.1589 and so we can write:

$$-0.1589 = -\frac{1}{RC} \Rightarrow RC = \frac{1}{0.1589} = 6.29\,\text{s}$$

d The difference between the stated and measured values for R is $(3.34 - 3.3)\,\text{k}\Omega$ = $0.04\,\text{k}\Omega$.

The percentage difference is therefore $(0.04\,\text{k}\Omega/3.3\,\text{k}\Omega) \times 100\% = 1.2\%$, which is well within the 2% tolerance stated.

e Taking $R = 334\,\text{k}\Omega$ and using the value for RC calculated in c we get:

$$C = \frac{6.29}{334 \times 10^3} = 1.88 \times 10^{-5}\,\text{F} = 19\,\mu\text{F}$$

Although the last two values of p.d. are only to 1 s.f. there are nine other data points to 2 or 3 s.f. on a good straight line. An answer to 2 s.f. is therefore justified.

f Percentage uncertainty in RC = % uc in R = 1.2% = % uc in C

Absolute uncertainty in $C = 19\,\mu\text{F} \times 1.2\% = 0.2\,\mu\text{F}$

However, as we can only express C to 2 s.f. we should write the value as:

$$RC = 19\,\mu\text{F} \pm 1\,\mu\text{F}$$

The maximum value that C could have is therefore $20\,\mu\text{F}$. This differs from the value of $22\,\mu\text{F}$ by $[(22 - 20)\,\mu\text{F}/22\,\mu\text{F}] \times 100\% = 9\%$.

The value of $22\,\mu\text{F}$ is a 'nominal' value and could be subject to a manufacturing tolerance of at least 10%. Therefore, it is quite possible that the capacitor is of nominal value $22\,\mu\text{F}$.

Knowledge check 79

What is the current in the capacitor in the worked example when it just starts to discharge?

Exam tip

Note that a discussion should include appropriate numerical data to support your argument.

PAG 10 Investigating simple harmonic motion

In this practical activity group (PAG) you may have done a number of experiments to investigate simple harmonic motion (SHM) for a range of different oscillating systems. Typical activities include:

- investigating the factors affecting simple harmonic motion
- observing forced and damped oscillations
- comparing static and dynamic methods to determine spring stiffness

This PAG gives you the opportunity to use digital instruments to measure time; to use analogue apparatus to measure distance and to interpolate between scale markings; to use methods to increase the accuracy of your measurements; and to use ICT to collect and process data.

Investigating the factors affecting the period of a simple harmonic oscillator

Essential theory

A mass m oscillating on a light vertical spring that obeys Hooke's law and has a spring constant k will execute SHM. The time period of the oscillations is given by:

$$T = 2\pi\sqrt{\frac{m}{k}}$$

A mass m swinging on a light inextensible string of length l at small angles of displacement will execute SHM. The time period of the oscillations is given by:

$$T = 2\pi\sqrt{\frac{l}{g}}$$

where g is the acceleration due to gravity.

Planning: mass oscillating on a spring

The exact procedure that you use will depend on which system you are investigating. See PAG 11 on page 88 for more information about planning an investigation.

Figure 61 shows a typical arrangement.

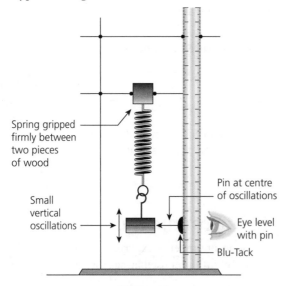

Spring gripped firmly between two pieces of wood

Small vertical oscillations

Pin at centre of oscillations

Eye level with pin

Blu-Tack

Figure 61

- The experiment works well with a standard 20 mm spring. You should be careful not to stretch it beyond its elastic limit.
- You also need a range of 100 g masses and a 50 g mass so that the spring can be loaded up to about 400 g in intervals of 50 g.
- A stopwatch is used for timing.
- The mass is gently pulled down and a number of oscillations are timed using a fiducial marker.

Simple pendulum

- A pendulum bob is attached to a string about 1.5 m long.
- Displace the bob a small distance to the side and release. Time a number of oscillations to obtain the time period of the swing.
- Reduce the length of the string and repeat the measurement of the time period.

Safety

For both oscillating systems, the clamp stand should be secure to prevent it from toppling.

For the mass-on-a-spring system, a soft surface should be placed under the masses in case they drop.

Worked example

Table 20 shows a typical set of data for an oscillating mass-on-a-spring system.

Table 20

m/kg	0.100	0.150	0.200	0.250	0.300	0.350	0.400
Time for 20 oscillations/s	8.20	10.04	11.48	12.96	14.20	15.34	16.38
T/s	0.410	0.502	0.574	0.648	0.710	0.767	0.819
T^2/s^2	0.168	0.252					

a Discuss why using a graph of T^2 on the y-axis against m on the x-axis is a better way of determining the spring constant than by plotting a graph of T against m.

b Estimate the percentage uncertainty in the value of T^2 for the 0.100 kg mass.

c Suggest another method of timing the oscillations that would remove the uncertainty due to human reaction time.

d Complete the table and plot a graph of T^2 against m.

e Use the gradient of your graph to obtain a value for the spring constant k of the spring.

Answer

a A graph of T^2 against m will give a straight line, whereas a graph of T against m will be a curve. As it is much easier to draw a line of best fit for points that lie on a straight line, a graph of T^2 against m is better.

b Although the time for 20 oscillations ($20T$) is recorded to 0.01 s, human reaction time is likely to be at least 0.1 s. Therefore:

% uc in $20T$ (8.20 s) = (0.1 s/8.20 s) × 100% = 1.2%

This will also be the percentage uncertainty in T, so:

% uc in T^2 = 2 × % uc in T = 2 × 1.2% = 2.4%

c The oscillations could be timed using a position sensor linked to a data logger placed underneath the oscillating mass.

d The remaining values of T^2/s^2 are: 0.32, 0.42, 0.50, 0.59, 0.67. Your graph should be a straight line through the origin with a gradient of 1.68 s^2 kg^{-1}.

→

Knowledge check 81

Explain why you should allow the pendulum to make two or three oscillations before you start timing.

Knowledge check 82

A mass of 300 g is suspended from a spring, causing it to extend by 110 mm. When the mass is gently pulled down and released, it makes 20 oscillations in 13.4 s. Use these data to determine *two* values for the spring constant k of the spring.

e Rearranging the equation for an oscillating mass gives:

$$T^2 = \frac{4\pi^2}{k}m \Rightarrow \frac{T^2}{m} = \frac{4\pi^2}{k}$$

$$\text{gradient} = \frac{4\pi^2}{k} \Rightarrow k = \frac{4\pi^2}{1.68\,\text{s}^2\,\text{kg}^{-1}} = 23.5\,\text{kg}\,\text{s}^{-2}$$

PAG 11 Investigation

This practical activity group (PAG) allows you to plan, carry out and analyse your own investigation. There are many different areas of physics that allow these skills to be developed. Your teacher may have provided equipment and some basic instructions on one particular topic, or, alternatively, you may have selected and designed your own investigation.

You will have:

- determined the variables to control and measure
- identified a method to collect suitable data
- designed a results table
- analysed, interpreted and presented your results

Determination of the specific heat capacity of a material

Essential theory

When a material is heated, the average kinetic energy of the particles increases, leading to an increase in the temperature of the material. The temperature change $\Delta\theta$ depends on the mass m of the material, the energy transferred ΔE and the specific heat capacity of the material c:

$$\Delta E = mc\Delta\theta$$

You should also recall that when a hot liquid or solid is placed into a cold liquid, the two will tend towards thermal equilibrium. The internal energy transferred from the hot object will be equal to the thermal energy gained by the cold liquid and its container, plus the thermal energy dissipated to the surroundings. Figure 62 illustrates this 'method of mixtures' for two liquids.

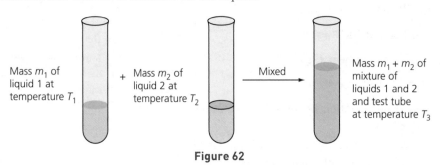

Mass m_1 of liquid 1 at temperature T_1

+ Mass m_2 of liquid 2 at temperature T_2

Mixed

Mass $m_1 + m_2$ of mixture of liquids 1 and 2 and test tube at temperature T_3

Figure 62

> ### Knowledge check 83
>
> A 2.0 kW kettle is used to heat 800 g of water for 1.0 minute. The water is initially at 20°C. Show that the final temperature of the water is about 56°C. [Use 4200 J kg^{-1} K^{-1} for the specific heat capacity of water.]

> ### Knowledge check 84
>
> A cooking recipe requires 600 ml of lukewarm water (between 36°C and 40°C). To achieve this, the cook adds 200 ml of warm water at 55°C from a kettle to 400 ml of cold water at 10°C. Show that the resulting mixture will be lukewarm. Assume that 1 ml of water has a mass of 1 g and that there are no energy transfers to the surroundings.

Planning

You need to take the following steps when planning an investigation.

■ Identify the relevant theory, and the variables that will have an effect on your measurements. Consider what data you will need to collect, and what variables you will need to control when doing so.

■ Research different methods that could be used to collect the data.

■ Choose one method for your experiment. You will need to know what apparatus is available for you to use in order to make a sensible choice.

■ Consider health and safety issues — and if there any specific precautions that you will need to take into account.

■ Decide what is the best way to record the data you will collect. Draft a table of results or set the parameters on the data logging equipment as appropriate.

■ Decide how you will analyse your data.

Safety

This will depend on the practical investigation chosen.

Worked example

A student chooses to measure the specific heat capacity of the material of a metal block using the method of mixtures. She has the following apparatus available to her:

■ three small rectangular aluminium blocks of different sizes

■ a waterproof electrical heater

■ Bunsen burner, tripod and gauze

■ glass beakers (size 50 ml, 250 ml and 1000 ml)

■ 100 ml measuring cylinder

■ 250 ml expanded polystyrene cup

■ calorimeter with insulated jacket and stirrer

■ three thermometers (range −50°C to +50°C, −10°C to +100°C, and −10°C to +110°C)

■ a data logger and temperature sensor (range −40°C to +125°C with a tolerance of ±0.5°C)

■ glass rods, metal lab tongs, bubble wrap, string, scissors, digital scales reading to 0.1 g, stopwatch

a Design a laboratory experiment to measure the specific heat capacity of aluminium. Include a labelled diagram and a method, and justify your choice of apparatus.

b Identify any variables that need to be controlled during the experiment.

c What are the main safety precautions required for the experiment?

d Explain how the student should analyse the data collected.

e Discuss possible sources of uncertainty and error in the experiment. →

Answer

a There are a number of different ways that the specific heat capacity could be measured. Figure 63 shows the apparatus used by the student in this case.

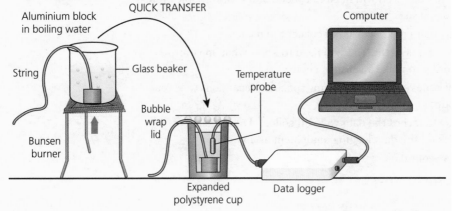

Figure 63

- The mass of the largest aluminium block is found using the digital scales.
- The aluminium block is suspended in a beaker of boiling water for 15 minutes — although a Bunsen burner is indicated, this could be done equally well using an electrical heater.
- Using the digital scales, a known mass of water is added to the expanded polystyrene cup.
- The temperature sensor and data logger are set to measure the temperature of the water in the polystyrene cup every 1.0 s for 30 minutes.
- After starting the temperature sensor, the aluminium block is quickly transferred into the water in the polystyrene cup. Care is taken to try to avoid transferring any water with the block.
- The water is stirred regularly to ensure mixing.
- This whole procedure is repeated for the other aluminium blocks.

This choice of apparatus was made for the following reasons.

- A water bath will ensure that the block is heated to a known temperature.
- Using a digital balance will enable the mass of water to be determined to a greater precision than using a measuring cylinder to determine its volume.
- The expanded polystyrene cup will absorb very little energy due to its small mass and poor conductivity.
- The expanded polystyrene cup, together with the bubble wrap lid, will reduce the loss of energy to the surroundings.
- Suspending the block on string, instead of using tongs, will reduce risk of scalding and will also minimise energy transfer by conduction to the unheated metal tongs.
- Data logging equipment enables a large number of readings to be taken at regular intervals and reduces possible errors due to reading the thermometer.

b The following variables need to be controlled.

- The temperature of the blocks must be 100°C — so the time for which the blocks are heated needs to be sufficiently long to ensure the largest block reaches 100°C. It does not matter if the smaller blocks are heated for longer than needed because the temperature will not go above 100°C. →

Exam tip

A preliminary experiment could be carried out to find out how long it takes for thermal equilibrium to be reached after the block has been transferred to the cup of water. That time can then be used to decide how often and how long to take measurements for using the data logger.

- The method of transfer, and the time it takes, should be the same for each block.
- Data should be recorded until the measured temperature of the water in the calorimeter remains constant for a few minutes, i.e. until thermal equilibrium is reached.

c The main safety risk is burns and scalds from the water (steam) and metal blocks, so:
  - once heated, the blocks should not be handled
  - hands should be kept out of the steam during transfer of the blocks

  Standard precautions for using a Bunsen burner should also be taken.

d The specific heat capacity of each block is found using the mass of the aluminium block m_a and its temperature change $\Delta\theta_a$ ($100°C$ – final temperature), the mass of the water in the expanded polystyrene cup m_w, and its temperature change $\Delta\theta_w$ (final temperature – temperature before block is added).

Energy lost by the aluminium block $= m_a c_a \Delta\theta_a$

Energy gained by the water $= m_w c_w \Delta\theta_w$

By the conservation of energy:

$$m_a c_a \Delta\theta_a = m_w c_w \Delta\theta_w \Rightarrow c_a = \frac{m_w c_w \Delta\theta_w}{m_a \Delta\theta_a}$$

A mean value of specific heat capacity is then calculated using the data from all three blocks.

e The uncertainty in the experiment will be due to:
  - digital scales $\pm0.1\,g$
  - temperature readings $\pm0.5°C$

Possible errors:
  - all of the block may not be at $100°C$
  - the block cooling down as it is transferred to the cup of water
  - not waiting long enough for thermal equilibrium to be reached
  - the energy absorbed by the cup may not be negligible
  - a small amount of energy may be transferred to the surroundings

Exam tip

Remember that uncertainties and errors are two different concepts. Errors refer to the difference between the measurement of a physics quantity and the 'true value' of that quantity. We can identify and minimise these where possible. The uncertainty is a measure of the spread of values. This may include the 'true value' provided the errors are not too large. For example, in this experiment, if the error due to the block cooling down during transfer is large, the spread of values for the specific heat capacity may not include the true value.

There are a number of not insignificant errors associated with method of mixtures experiments and so electrical methods for determining the specific heat capacities for solids and liquids are usually preferred, as indicated in the OCR specification.

Knowledge check 85

If the block loses a significant amount of energy to the surroundings during the transfer process, explain what effect this would have on the value obtained for the specific heat capacity of aluminium.

PAG 12 Research skills

This practical activity group (PAG) is quite different from the other practical activity groups. It allows you to develop the research skills that are used by many physicists working in industry and academia. You will make use of secondary sources (e.g. books, journals and the internet) to find information about a topic and then present that information in a suitable form.

During your A-level course you may have had opportunity to research different topics, including:

- presentation on materials, linking the properties of a material with practical applications of that material
- a research report containing an in-depth study of an area of physics taught during your A-level course
- a research report containing an in-depth study of the social and ethical issues arising from an area of physics, or the historical development of knowledge

Essential theory

The theory required will depend on your choice of topic during each activity.

Planning

A key part of research using secondary sources is choosing suitable sources, then keeping a detailed list of sources and being able to evaluate the quality of the sources you have used.

Start your research by looking for general references linked to your topic. Popular science journals and books may contain useful information as a starting point.

A popular starting point on the internet is *Wikipedia*. In itself, *Wikipedia* is not a good source to reference, but it can provide an overview of a topic and a list of other references to read.

When you are looking for sources and information, avoid the temptation to 'cut and paste' huge chunks of webpages. It is far better to read the webpage and make brief notes about the key information in a separate document, including the reference to the web address and when you visited the site.

Google Scholar (scholar.google.co.uk) allows more detailed references to be found. This allows you to find journal papers linked to your topic.

Referencing

The purpose of including references in reports is to give the sources of information that you have used, and to enable people reading your work to find out more information should they wish to. It also prevents suggestions of plagiarism.

Different academic disciplines have different ways to reference research materials. You should use the reference system that your school recommends. The OCR Practical Skills Handbook provides information about two reference systems: Vancouver and Harvard.

Exam tip

When using a search engine, using '.pdf' as part of your search term will return results that are available for download. This can be particularly helpful with academic papers, some of which are not generally available.

Questions & Answers

The OCR examinations

Both the OCR A and B specifications for the A-level physics examination consist of three papers. All papers will examine practical skills in physics. This will include:

- *Planning*: solving problems set in a practical context, identification of variables and evaluating experimental methods.
- *Implementing*: experiencing a wide variety of practical work, developing practical and investigative skills, using the correct units for measurements and presenting data in an appropriate format.
- *Analysis*: processing, analysing and interpreting experimental results, using appropriate mathematical skills, including significant figures, and plotting and interpreting graphs from experimental results.
- *Evaluation*: using data to draw conclusions, including knowledge of errors and uncertainties, identifying anomalies in measurements and limitations in experimental procedure, and suggesting improvements to experimental procedures and apparatus.

In specification B, although all papers may include questions in a practical context, paper 3 will have a particular emphasis on practical skills, including data analysis.

This student guide covers only practical work, mainly through consideration of the 12 practical activity groups. Therefore, the questions in this section only reflect the type of question that will be set to *test your understanding of experimental methods* and are *not* representative of the papers as a whole.

In the AS examination there are just two papers and questions based on practical work may be set in both papers.

A data sheet is provided with each examination. Copies may be downloaded from the OCR website, or can be found at the end of past papers. Section 5c of the specification is a copy of the data sheet.

Examiners use certain **command terms** that require you to respond in a particular way, for example 'state', 'explain' or 'discuss'. You must be able to distinguish between these terms and understand exactly what each requires you to do. Some commonly used terms are:

- Assess — Give careful consideration to all the factors or events that apply, and identify which are the most important or relevant. Make a judgement on the importance of something, and come to a conclusion where needed.
- Compare and contrast — Look for the similarities of and differences between two (or more) things. This should not require the drawing of a conclusion. The answer must relate to both (or all) things mentioned in the question. The answer must include at least one similarity and one difference.

Questions & Answers

- Criticise — Inspect a set of data, an experimental plan or a scientific statement and consider the elements. Look at the merits and/or faults of the information presented, and back any judgements made.
- Deduce — Draw/reach conclusion(s) from the information provided.
- Derive — Combine two or more equations or principles to develop a new equation.
- Describe — Give an account of something. Statements in the response need to be developed, as they are often linked, but do not need to include a justification or reason.
- Determine — The answer must have an element that is quantitative from the stimulus provided, or must show how the answer can be reached quantitatively.
- Devise — Plan or invent a procedure from existing principles/ideas.
- Discuss — Identify the issue/situation/problem/argument that is being assessed within the question. Explore all aspects of the issue/etc. Investigate the issue/etc. by reasoning or argument.
- Evaluate — Review information, then bring it together to form a conclusion, drawing on evidence, including strengths, weaknesses, alternative actions, relevant data or information. Come to a supported judgement of a subject's qualities and relation to its context.
- Explain — Requires justification/exemplification of a point. The answer must contain some element of reasoning/justification, which can include mathematical explanations.
- Give/State/Name — Generally requires recall of one or more pieces of information.
- Identify — Usually requires some key information to be selected from a given stimulus/resource.
- Justify — Give evidence to support (either the statement given in the question or an earlier answer).
- Plot — Produce a graph by marking points accurately on a grid from data that are provided and then drawing a line of best fit through these points. A suitable scale and appropriately labelled axes must be included if these are not provided in the question.
- Predict — Give an expected result.
- Show that — Prove that a numerical figure is as stated in the question. The answer must be to at least one more significant figure than the numerical figure in the question.
- Sketch — Produce a freehand drawing. For a graph, this would require a line and labelled axes, with important features indicated; the axes are not scaled.

You should pay particular attention to drawing diagrams, plotting graphs and making calculations. Many candidates lose marks by failing to label diagrams properly, not giving essential data on graphs and, in calculations, by not showing all the working or by omitting units.

The answers that follow should not be treated as model answers — they represent the bare minimum necessary to gain the marks. Some questions have tips on how to answer the question, preceded by ⓔ. Comments (denoted by ⓔ) may either provide you with useful tips or indicate where many candidates lose marks. Ticks (✓) are included in the answers to show where marks are awarded.

■ Practice questions

Multiple choice

Question 1

A student records the diameter of a wire five times using a micrometer reading to 0.01 mm. The readings are 1.17 mm, 1.19 mm, 1.17 mm, 1.16 mm and 1.18 mm. The student averages these readings but does not take into account the zero error on the micrometer. The average measurement of the diameter is:

A precise and accurate

C accurate but not precise

B precise but not accurate

D not accurate and not precise   (1 mark)

Question 2

A student is measuring the force on a current-carrying conductor using the apparatus shown in Figure 1. He measures the length of the copper wire in the magnetic field using a 30 cm rule, which has markings every millimetre.

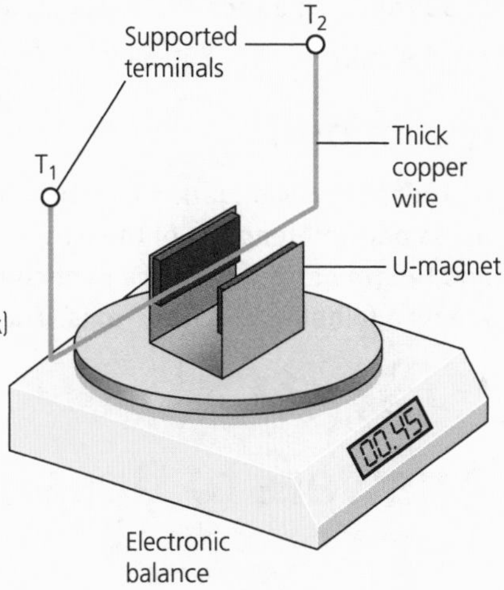

The uncertainty in this measurement of length is:

A ±1 cm   **B** ±0.5 cm   **C** ±0.2 cm   **D** ±0.05 cm   (1 mark)

Question 3

In an experiment to determine the specific latent heat of vaporisation of water, steam is condensed in water at room temperature. A student records the initial and final temperatures of the water as $\theta_i = (19.0 \pm 0.5)°C$ and $\theta_f = (29.0 \pm 0.5)°C$. The percentage uncertainty in the temperature difference $\Delta\theta$ is:

A 3%   **B** 5%   **C** 10%   **D** 20%   (1 mark)

Supported terminals

T_1

T_2

Thick copper wire

U-magnet

Electronic balance

Figure 1

Question 4

An object falls from rest with an acceleration g. The variation with time t of the displacement s of the object is given by $s = \frac{1}{2}gt^2$. The uncertainty in the value of t is ±3% and the uncertainty in the value of s is ±2%. The best estimate for the uncertainty of the value of g is:

A 5%   **B** 6%   **C** 8%   **D** 11%   (1 mark)

Question 5

A student measures the wavelength of a laser using a pair of slits of separation a. Interference fringes are produced on a white screen placed at a distance D from the slits. The separation of the fringes is x.

The slits are replaced by new slits of separation $a/2$ and the screen distance is doubled to $2D$. The new fringe separation is:

A $x/2$ **B** x **C** $2x$ **D** $4x$ (1 mark)

Question 6

(A-level only) A student is investigating the absorption of gamma rays by lead. With no absorber, the count rate, when corrected for background, is $400\,min^{-1}$. When a lead disc is placed between the source and detector, the count rate falls to $300\,min^{-1}$. If a second, identical, disc is added, the count rate will drop to:

A $150\,min^{-1}$ **B** $200\,min^{-1}$ **C** $225\,min^{-1}$ **D** $250\,min^{-1}$ (1 mark)

Question 7

A student is investigating how the frequency of a stretched wire depends on the mass per unit length μ of the wire using wires of different diameter. The tension and length of each wire are kept constant. The student plots a graph of $\ln f$ on the y-axis against $\ln \mu$ on the x-axis. The gradient will be:

A $-\dfrac{1}{\sqrt{2}}$ **B** $-\dfrac{1}{2}$ **C** $\dfrac{1}{2}$ **D** $\dfrac{1}{\sqrt{2}}$ (1 mark)

Answers to Questions 1–7

1 B

🅔 The repeated readings are close to each other, which means they are *precise*. The student neglected to take into account the zero error, and therefore each reading may larger or smaller than the true reading. The readings are therefore *not accurate*.

2 C

🅔 As the measurement of length will be the difference of two readings, each to an uncertainty of 0.1 cm, the uncertainty in the length will be 2 × 0.1 cm = 0.2 cm. The uncertainty of each reading could be taken as 0.05 cm, giving an overall uncertainty of 0.1 cm, but that is not one of the possible answers.

3 C

🅔 When a value is found by adding or subtracting two quantities, the maximum and minimum possible values have to be calculated to find the uncertainty in the value and then the percentage uncertainty can be calculated.

4 C

🄔 Remember to add the percentage uncertainty if quantities are divided; and if a quantity is raised to a power, multiply the percentage uncertainty by the power. Then: % uc in g = (% uc in s) + (2 × % uc in t).

5 D

🄔 Use $x = \lambda D/a$. Practise using ratios — they are common in multiple-choice questions.

6 C

🄔 With one disc, the count rate reduces to $300\,\text{min}^{-1} = 0.75 \times 400\,\text{min}^{-1}$. So, for two discs, the count rate will decrease to $0.75 \times 300\,\text{min}^{-1} = 225\,\text{min}^{-1}$. This is a quick way of checking whether a graph is exponential.

7 B

🄔 From $f = \dfrac{1}{2l}\sqrt{\dfrac{T}{\mu}} \Rightarrow f = \dfrac{\sqrt{T}}{2l} \times \dfrac{1}{\sqrt{\mu}} = \dfrac{\sqrt{T}}{2l} \times \mu^{-1/2} \Rightarrow \ln f = \ln\left(\dfrac{\sqrt{T}}{2l}\right) - \dfrac{1}{2}\ln\mu$

You need to practise taking logs of equations such as this. Although you could also take logs to base 10 ('log' on your calculator) when trying to find a power, if you *always* take natural logs ('ln'), you will not get the wrong logs when dealing with exponential functions (which *must* be 'ln').

Structured questions

Question 8

A rectangular glass block is measured with a ruler calibrated in 1 mm divisions:

        length = 11.5 cm   **width = 6.2 cm**   **depth = 3.1 cm**

(a) Calculate the volume of the block.   (1 mark)

(b) Estimate the percentage uncertainty and hence the absolute uncertainty in your value.   (3 marks)

(c) State how the volume of the block should be recorded.   (1 mark)

        Total: 5 marks

Student answer

(a) volume = $11.5\,\text{cm} \times 6.2\,\text{cm} \times 3.1\,\text{cm} = 221.03\,\text{cm}^3 = 221\,\text{cm}^3$ ✓

(b) % uc in volume = % uc in length + % uc in width + % uc in depth

    = (0.1 cm/11.5 cm) × 100% + (0.1 cm/6.2 cm) × 100% + (0.1 cm/3.1 cm) × 100% ✓

    = (0.870 + 1.61 + 3.23)% = 5.7% ✓

    Absolute uncertainty in volume = 5.7% of $221\,\text{cm}^3 = 13\,\text{cm}^3$ ✓

🄔 Remember that the percentage uncertainties are added when quantities are multiplied.

(c) volume of block = (221 ± 13) cm³ ✓

℮ Although the width and depth are only measured to 2 s.f., an answer of 221 ± 13 cm³ is arguably better than giving the answer as 220 ± 10 cm³ to 2 s.f. Full credit would be given for either answer.

Question 9

A student is measuring the e.m.f. generated by a magnet falling through a coil of wire using a data logger and voltage sensor.

(a) Explain why using a data logger and voltage sensor is a good strategy.　　　(3 marks)

(b) After collecting her data, she realises that the sensor has a zero error. Explain what is meant by a zero error, and describe what she should do with her data to take the error into account.　　　(2 marks)

Total: 5 marks

Student answer

(a) The time for the magnet to fall through the coil is very short. ✓

Because a data logger can sample at a high rate, ✓ it can take a large number of readings in this short time. ✓

℮ The question says 'explain', so it is necessary to state that the time involved is small.

(b) Zero error means that the voltage sensor gives a non-zero reading when there is no measurement being taken. ✓

She should subtract the value of the non-zero reading from her e.m.f. data. ✓

Question 10

(A-level only) A student used the arrangement shown in Figure 2 to measure the specific heat capacity of water.

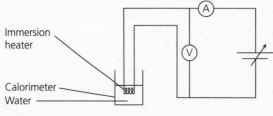

Figure 2

(a) State the measurements the student would need to make in order to measure the specific heat capacity of the water.　　　(2 marks)

(b) Explain how the student could try to make the measurements as accurate as possible. (4 marks)

(c) State *one* safety precaution you would take if you were to carry out this experiment. (1 mark)

Total: 7 marks

Student answer

(a) You would need to calculate the energy supplied electrically by measuring the current, p.d. and time of heating ✓ (or electrical energy supplied $W = VIt$ ✓).

You would also need to measure the mass and the initial and final temperatures of the water. ✓

(b) Points might include the following:

- Stir the liquid regularly to ensure that it is all at the same temperature.
- Record the final steady temperature after switching off to allow equilibrium to be attained.
- Determine the amount of energy absorbed by the container and deduct this from the energy supplied by the heater. This would give you the actual energy supplied to the liquid.
- Insulate the container to prevent energy being transferred to the surroundings.
- Leave the thermometer in the liquid to ensure that it is in thermal equilibrium with the water, and ensure that it is not touching the walls of the container.

Any two points ✓✓ explained ✓✓

---

e As the question asks you to 'explain', you must both state the technique *and* explain why it improves the accuracy. Note that using an expanded polystyrene beaker both provides insulation *and* avoids having to determine any energy taken by the container.

(c) Safety precautions could include:

- Make sure the wiring does not short circuit.
- Stand up at all times and clamp the beaker to avoid scalding in case the beaker of hot water is knocked over.
- Keep the immersion heater fully immersed.

Any one ✓

Question 11

Figure 3 shows an oscilloscope trace of a sound wave. The signal has a frequency of 2.5 kHz and a peak voltage of 500 mV.

(a) What are the time base and voltage settings on the oscilloscope? (3 marks)

ⓔ This question is based on PAG 5. You are expected to be familiar with the use of an oscilloscope.

(b) The speed of sound is 330 m s^{-1}. What is the wavelength of this sound wave? (1 mark)

(c) (A-level only) Determine the root mean square voltage displayed on the oscilloscope. (2 marks)

Total: 6 marks

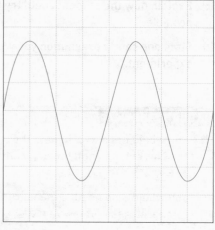

Figure 3

Student answer

(a) $T = 1/f = 1/(2500\,s^{-1}) = 4.00 \times 10^{-4}\,s$ ✓ $= 400\,\mu s$

   T = time for one wavelength = four divisions ✓ time base = 100 µs/div ✓

   V_{peak} = 500 mV = 2.5 divisions ✓ voltage setting = 500 mV/2.5 div = 200 mV/div ✓

ⓔ To get full marks, you would be expected to express the time base in realistic units — either (preferably) µs/div or ms/div and not 10^{-4} s/div

(b) $c = f\lambda \Rightarrow \lambda = c/f = 330\,m\,s^{-1}/2500\,s^{-1} = 0.132\,m$ (or 13 cm) ✓

(c) $V_{rms} = \dfrac{V_{peak}}{\sqrt{2}}$ ✓ $\Rightarrow V_{rms} = \dfrac{500\,mV}{\sqrt{2}} = 350\,mV$ ✓

Question 12

A student is investigating the resistance R of some conductive modelling putty, which was shaped into a cylinder of length l. He suggests that the relationship between the resistivity ρ of the putty with volume V is given by: $\rho = \dfrac{RV}{l^2}$

The student decides to plot a graph with R on the y-axis and l^2 on the x-axis.

(a) Explain why this is a sensible decision. (1 mark)

(b) The student obtained the graph shown in Figure 4.
   (i) Draw a line of best fit and determine the gradient of this line.
   (ii) Determine the uncertainty in your value of gradient. Use an appropriate number of significant figures in your answer. (6 marks)

(c) The student used 26.8 cm^3 of putty in the experiment. Calculate the resistivity of the putty. (3 marks)

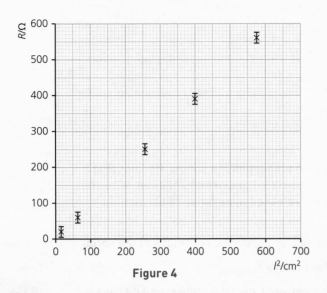

Figure 4

Total: 10 marks

Student answer

(a) This will produce a straight-line graph with gradient ρ/V. ✓

(b) (i) $\quad \text{gradient} = \dfrac{(600-0)\ \Omega}{(620-0)\ \text{cm}^2} = 0.97\ \Omega\ \text{cm}^{-2}$ ✓✓

e Note that a mark is given for drawing a *large* triangle

(ii) Draw two lines as shown and calculate their gradients. This will provide the maximum and minimum likely gradient. ✓

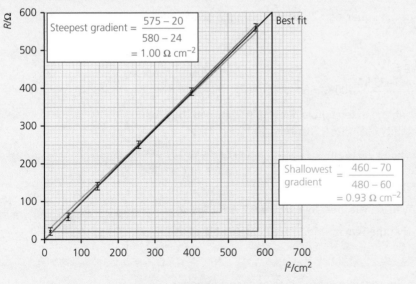

The uncertainty is half the difference between these two values.

In this case, ½ × (1.00 − 0.93) = 0.035 Ω cm^{-2} ✓

Uncertainty in gradient = ±0.04 Ω cm^{-2} ✓

(c) gradient $= \rho/V \Rightarrow \rho =$ gradient $\times V$ ✓

$\rho = 9.7 \times 10^3 \, \Omega \, m^{-2} \times 26.8 \times 10^{-6} \, m^3 = 0.26 \, \Omega \, m$ ✓✓

ⓔ Watch the units. It is probably best to convert the gradient and volume to metres before doing the final calculation.

Question 13

(A-level only) A student is investigating the properties of a spring. He finds that a mass of 300 g suspended from the spring causes it to extend by 120 mm. When he pulls the mass down a small distance and releases it, he times 20 oscillations in 14.12 s using a digital stopwatch.

(a) Use these data to determine *two* values for the spring constant k of the spring. (4 marks)

(b) Show that the unit $N \, m^{-1}$ is equivalent to $kg \, s^{-2}$. (1 mark)

(c) Calculate the percentage difference between your two values, and discuss which value is likely to have the greater uncertainty. (4 marks)

(d) Explain why it is important to pull the mass down only a small distance. (2 marks)

Total: 11 marks

Student answer

(a) $F = kx \Rightarrow k = F/x = (0.300 \, kg \times 9.8 \, N \, kg^{-1})/0.120 \, m$ ✓ $= 24.5 \, N \, m^{-1}$ ✓

$T = 2\pi\sqrt{\dfrac{m}{k}} \Rightarrow k = \dfrac{4\pi^2 m}{T^2} = \dfrac{4\pi^2 \times 0.300 \, kg}{(0.706 \, s)^2}$ ✓ $= 23.8 \, kg \, s^{-2}$ ✓

ⓔ Marks are often lost by either not squaring π or by forgetting to divide the time by the number of oscillations to find T.

(b) $N \, m^{-1} = (kg \, m \, s^{-2}) \times m^{-1} = kg \, s^{-2}$ ✓

(c) percentage difference $= \dfrac{24.5 - 23.8}{24.2} \times 100\% = 3\%$ ✓

The uncertainty in measuring the extension is likely to be 2 mm at the most, giving a percentage uncertainty of $(2 \, mm/120 \, mm) \times 100\% = 1.7\%$ ✓

Although the time is recorded to 0.01 s, in reality the uncertainty is governed by human reaction time, say 0.1 s, giving a percentage uncertainty in T of $(0.1 \, s/14.12 \, s) \times 100\% = 0.7\%$. ✓

The percentage uncertainty in T^2 will therefore be $2 \times 0.7\% = 1.4\%$. ✓

It would therefore appear that the two methods are comparable in terms of uncertainty.

ⓔ It is important that you can make sensible estimations of uncertainties. A common mistake here would be to quote the uncertainty in the timing as 0.01 s when reaction time is likely to be 0.1 s. Remember, the percentage uncertainty is *doubled* if the quantity is *squared*, and the *average* value should be used in the denominator when determining the percentage difference between two *experimental* values.

(d) For simple harmonic motion, the acceleration and, therefore, the force must be proportional to the displacement. ✓ The spring should be given a *small* displacement to ensure that it oscillates within the Hooke's law region, so that force ∝ displacement. ✓

Question 14

Figure 5 shows an arrangement that a student sets up to investigate the acceleration of a glider on a tilted air track. For clarity, the lamps illuminating the light gates have been omitted.

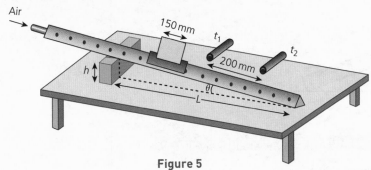

Figure 5

(a) The glider is released from rest and the interrupter card, of length 150 mm, is timed as it passes through the two light gates. Times of $t_1 = 1.49$ s and $t_2 = 0.24$ s are recorded.

   (i) Calculate the average velocities v_1 and v_2 of the glider as it passes through each light gate.

   (ii) The light gates are 200 mm apart. Calculate the acceleration of the glider.

ⓔ Using $v^2 = u^2 + 2as$ instead of $v = u + at$ is an alternative way of determining an acceleration when investigating motion.

   (iii) Show that the theoretical acceleration of the glider is $g\sin\theta$, where θ is the angle that the track makes with the horizontal.

   (iv) The student measures the angle by means of a protractor. She records a value of 6.0° ± 0.5°. Determine a value for g from the data recorded by the student.

   (v) Estimate the uncertainty in this value for g. What conclusion can you come to regarding the validity of this experiment?

   (vi) Suggest why the value of acceleration obtained is likely to be too small.   (10 marks)

(b) The student's teacher suggests that a much better way to determine θ would be by measuring the distances h and L as shown in Figure 5. The student records $h = 98 \pm 1$ mm and $L = 1000 \pm 1$ mm. What value does this give for θ? Comment on this value.   (4 marks)

(c) Explain how you could extend this experiment to get a more reliable value for g. Include a sketch of the graph you would plot and how you would find g from it. Explain how your graph would reduce both systematic and random errors.   (6 marks)

Total: 20 marks

Student answer

(a) (i) $v_1 = 0.150\,\text{m}/1.49\,\text{s} = 0.101\,\text{m}\,\text{s}^{-1}$ and $v_2 = 0.150\,\text{m}/0.24\,\text{s} = 0.625\,\text{m}\,\text{s}^{-1}$ ✓

(ii) $v^2 = u^2 + 2as \Rightarrow a = \dfrac{v_2^2 - v_1^2}{2s} \Rightarrow a = \dfrac{\left(0.625\,\text{ms}^{-1}\right)^2 - \left(0.101\,\text{ms}^{-1}\right)^2}{2 \times 0.200\,\text{m}}$ ✓

$a = 0.95(1)\,\text{m}\,\text{s}^{-2}$ ✓

(iii) Refer to the free-body diagram for the glider below.

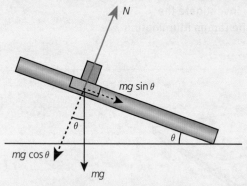

Force on glider F = component of mg down the plane = $mg\sin\theta$. ✓

$F = ma \Rightarrow a = F/m = (mg\sin\theta)/m = g\sin\theta$. ✓

(iv) $a = g\sin\theta \Rightarrow g = a/\sin\theta = 0.951\,\text{m}\,\text{s}^{-2}/\sin 6.0° = 9.1\,\text{m}\,\text{s}^{-2}$ ✓

(v) Largest and smallest possible values for g are:

$0.951\,\text{m}\,\text{s}^{-2}/\sin 5.5° = 9.9\,\text{m}\,\text{s}^{-2}$ and $0.951\,\text{m}\,\text{s}^{-2}/\sin 6.5° = 8.4\,\text{m}\,\text{s}^{-1}$ ✓

Uncertainty in g = ½ × (9.9 – 8.4) = ±0.8 m s^{-2} ✓

The accepted value of $g = 9.8\,\text{m}\,\text{s}^{-2}$ just falls within this (large) uncertainty, so the value of g obtained suggests that the experiment could be valid. ✓

(vi) The value obtained is likely to be too small because there is almost certain to be some frictional force slowing down the glider. ✓

(b) $\tan\theta = h/L = 98\,\text{mm}/1000\,\text{mm} = 0.098 \Rightarrow \theta = \tan^{-1}(0.098) = 5.60°$ ✓

Largest value could be $\tan^{-1}(0.099) = 5.65°$ and smallest value $\tan^{-1}(0.097) = 5.54°$ ✓

So we can say $\theta = 5.60° \pm 0.05°$, ✓ which is a far (10 times) greater precision than using a protractor. ✓

ⓔ Choosing the right instrument, or technique, for making a measurement, and understanding its limitations, are important skills that you should develop during the course of your practical work.

(c) The angle of the track should be varied to give different values of θ (or tan θ). ✓

A graph of a against tan θ should be plotted, ✓ which should be a straight line through the origin (sketch should show this). ✓

The gradient of this graph is g. ✓

The graph will reduce random errors by averaging several values. ✓

If there is a systematic error due to frictional forces, this will be indicated by a small intercept on the tan θ axis, but the gradient will still be g. ✓

e It is important that you understand how a graph can reduce random errors and show systematic errors.

Knowledge check answers

1 a $kg\,m^2\,s^{-2}$, **b** $A\,s$, **c** $kg\,m^2\,s^{-3}\,A^{-2}$, **d** $kg\,m^2\,s^{-3}$

2 Diameter = $1.27 \times 10^{-2}\,m$
Length = $0.800\,m$
Area = $1.27 \times 10^{-4}\,m^2$
Volume = $1.02 \times 10^{-4}\,m^3$

3 Wavelength = $6.43 \times 10^{-7}\,m$
Slit distance = $3.3 \times 10^{-6}\,m$

4 $c_w = \dfrac{c}{n_w}$ and $c_o = \dfrac{c}{n_o}$ so $c_w : c_o = n_o : n_w$

$c_w : c_o = 1.47 : 1.33 = 1.11$

5 a 48, **b** 300, **c** 8.0×10^3

6 $n = \sin 35.5°/\sin 26.0° = 1.32$

7

Angle	$\sin\theta$	$\cos\theta$	$\tan\theta$
$\theta = 0°$	0	1	0
$\theta = 45°$	0.707	0.707	1
$\theta = \pi\,rad$	0	−1	0
$\theta = \pi/2\,rad$	1	0	∞

8 a 1.08×10^{21}, **b** $3.0 \times 10^8\,m\,s^{-1}$, **c** 1.8×10^2 or 180

9 a 10^{18}, **b** 10^3, **c** 10^2, **d** 10^9

10 a Assume a popcorn is a cube of side $10^{-2}\,m$ or volume $10^{-6}\,m^3$
Assume the room is a cube of side $10\,m$ or volume $10^3\,m^3$
Number of pieces of popcorn = $10^3\,m^3/10^{-6}\,m^3 = 10^9$

b Assume you are made out of water. Number of electrons per molecule is 10^1.
Mass of 1 molecule of water is $10^{-27}\,kg$
Assume your mass is $10^2\,kg$
Number of molecules of water you contain = $10^2/10^{-27} = 10^{29}$
⇒ Number of electrons = $10^{29} \times 10^1 = 10^{30}$

c $E_p = mg\Delta h$
Assume Mount Everest is $10^5\,m$ high
$E_p = 10^2\,kg \times 10^1\,m\,s^{-2} \times 10^5\,m = 10^8\,J$
Assume the energy from a chocolate bar = $10^5\,J$
Number of bars = $10^8/10^5 = 10^3$

11 a $W = VQ$, **b** $x \propto F$, **c** $\Phi = BA$

12 a $V = \dfrac{m}{\rho}$

b $m = \dfrac{p}{v}$

c $R_2 = R_1\left(\dfrac{V_{out}}{V_{in} - V_{out}}\right)$

d $a = \dfrac{v^2 - u^2}{2s}$

e $\theta = \sin^{-1}\left(\dfrac{n\lambda}{d}\right)$

f $\omega = \sqrt{\dfrac{F}{mr}}$

13 a Moment = $225\,N \times 0.070\,m = 16\,N\,m$
b $L = x/\varepsilon = 0.10\,m/0.1 = 1\,m$
c $0.020\,m$ (remember to put your calculator in radian mode)

14 $s = ut + \frac{1}{2}at^2 \Rightarrow t^2 = 2h/g$
(as $u = 0$) $\Rightarrow t = 0.55\,s$

15 Acidity (pH)
Earthquake intensity (Richter scale)
Hardness (Mohs' scale)
Star brightness (magnitude)
Wind intensity (Beaufort scale)

16 a plot λ (y-axis) against $\dfrac{1}{f}$ (x-axis); gradient = c
b plot R (y-axis) against l (x-axis); gradient = $\dfrac{\rho}{A}$
c plot T^2 (y-axis) against m (x-axis); gradient = $\dfrac{4\pi^2}{k}$

17 Instantaneous acceleration = $(20\,m\,s^{-1} - 5.5\,m\,s^{-1})/(6.0\,s - 0.0\,s) = 2.4\,m\,s^{-2}$
Average acceleration = $17.5\,m\,s^{-1}/6.0\,s = 2.9\,m\,s^{-2}$

18 a Energy stored in a spring: $0.36\,J$–$0.38\,J$
b Charge: $3300\,\mu C$–$3400\,\mu C$

19 a graph a, **b** graph c, **c** graph d

20 Volume = $\pi r^2 h$
= $\pi \times (6.0 \times 10^{-3}\,m)^2 \times 1.50\,m = 1.7 \times 10^{-4}\,m^3$

21 Mass of one atom = molar mass/Avogadro constant
= $(12.0 \times 10^{-3}\,kg\,mol^{-1})/(6.02 \times 10^{23}\,mol^{-1})$
= $1.99 \times 10^{-26}\,kg$
Volume of one atom = mass/density
= $5.69 \times 10^{-30}\,m^3$
Assuming an atom is spherical:
$V = \dfrac{4}{3}\pi r^3$
$r = \sqrt[3]{\dfrac{3V}{4\pi}} = 1.1 \times 10^{-10}\,m$

22 a $0.262\,rad$, **b** $0.873\,rad$, **c** $2.53\,rad$

23 a $22.5°$, **b** $85.9°$, **c** $8.59°$

24

Angle	$\sin\theta$	$\cos\theta$	$\tan\theta$
$5.0\,rad$	−0.96	0.28	−3.4
$0.50\,rad$	0.48	0.88	0.55
$0.050\,rad$	0.050	1.0	0.050

25 There are many examples of random errors where measurements are affected in an unpredictable fashion: e.g. changes in room temperature, contact resistance, trying to read the current from an ammeter when the current is changing quickly, human reaction time when starting and stopping a stopwatch.

26 $0.86 - 0.02 = 0.84\,mm$

27 Accurate — how close to the true value a measurement is.
Precision — how close to each other repeated measurements are.

28 The range of data is large ($62\,mT - 46\,mT = 16\,mT$), giving a 16% variation either side of the mean value. The data are therefore not precise.

29 The smallest change in value that can be measured using the instrument.

30 Largest = $100 + 5\% = 105\,\Omega$
Smallest = $100 - 5\% = 95\,\Omega$

31 a Uncertainty in measurement = $0.1\,mm$.
Diameter = $21.5\,mm \pm 0.1\,mm$

b Percentage uncertainty =
($0.1\,mm/21.5\,mm$) × 100% = 0.5%

32 a Correct reading is $8.3\,cm$ (or $83\,mm$)

b With a mirror behind the pointer, move your head until the image is hidden by the pointer. Then you are reading the scale vertically, which will give you the correct value.

33 Vernier reads $12.27\,cm$ (or $122.7\,mm$)

34 Volume of sphere $V = \frac{4}{3}\pi r^3$

$V = \frac{4}{3} \times \pi \times (5.0 \times 10^{-3}\,m)^3 = 5.24 \times 10^{-7}\,m^3$

Density = mass/volume
= ($1.3 \times 10^{-3}\,kg$)/($5.24 \times 10^{-7}\,m^3$) = $2481\,kg\,m^{-3}$
= $2.5 \times 10^3\,kg\,m^{-3}$ or $2.5\,g\,cm^{-3}$ to 2 s.f. (in line with the data)

35 a $0.5\,mm$ (the bottom half of the main scale subdivides the $1\,mm$ divisions of the top half of the scale into $0.5\,mm$)

b $7.25\,mm$, assuming the micrometer reads zero when closed/there is no zero error

36 There is a positive zero error, so this must be subtracted from each reading. The actual diameter is therefore: $2.12\,mm - 0.03\,mm = 2.09\,mm$.

37 Random errors must be reduced. You should be able to analyse each source of random error in the experiment and suggest ways of reducing it. This will include taking repeats, but will also involve choosing apparatus with greater resolution or improving experimental technique.

38 Use vernier callipers (or a micrometer). Check for zero error. Then measure the diameter several times, at different angles, and average.
Radius = ½ × diameter. Then use the equation:
volume of a sphere $V = \frac{4}{3}\pi r^3$

39 a Human reaction time is at least $0.1\,s$, which is far more significant than the resolution of the stopwatch (typically $0.01\,s$) when measuring short times.

b Uncertainty = $\pm 0.1\,s$ (or possibly $\pm 0.2\,s$)

40 ($0.1\,s/18.9\,s$) × 100% = 0.53%

41 Use the set-square with one side on the bench to check that the vertical height of the beam above the bench is the same in different places along the length of the beam.

42 a $\sin\theta = 87\,mm/1000\,mm = 0.087 \Rightarrow \theta = 5.0°$

b Uncertainty in lengths = (say) $\pm 2\,mm$
% uc in height = ($2\,mm/87\,mm$) × 100% = 2.3%
% uc in length = ($2\,mm/1000\,mm$) × 100% = 0.2%
% uc in angle = 2.3% + 0.2% = 2.5%

43 $\frac{1}{2}mv^2 = mg\Delta h \Rightarrow v = \sqrt{2g\Delta h}$

$\Rightarrow v = \sqrt{2 \times 9.81 \times 0.10} = 1.4\,m\,s^{-1}$

44 ($1.44 + 1.42 + 1.46 + 1.43$)/4 = 1.44
1.56 is not included in the mean calculation because it is clearly anomalous.

45 $60\,s \times 0.5\,s^{-1} = 30$ measurements

46 Using $s = ut + \frac{1}{2}at^2$ where $u = 0$ and $a = 9.81\,m\,s^{-2}$:

$t = \sqrt{\dfrac{2s}{a}} = \sqrt{\dfrac{2 \times 0.05\,m}{9.81\,m\,s^{-2}}} = 0.101\,s$

$\approx 100\,ms$

47 Inconsistent decimal places in the first column. Incorrect column headings (should be p.d./V and Current/A). Units should not appear in the body of the table. Current only recorded to 1 s.f.

48 Mean $a = 0.453\,m\,s^{-2} = 0.45\,m\,s^{-2}$ to 2 s.f.

49 $120\,m = k \times 2000\,kg$
$x = k \times 1400\,kg$
$x = (1400\,kg/2000\,kg) \times 120\,m = 84\,m$

50 a Plot v^2 on the y-axis against h on the x-axis. The graph should be a straight line through the origin with gradient $2g$.

b Plot T^2 on the y-axis against l on the x-axis. The graph should be a straight line through the origin with gradient $4\pi^2/g$.

51 $R = V/I = (4.97 \times 10^{-3}\,V)/(22.6 \times 10^{-6}\,A) = 220\,\Omega$

52 a For a metallic conductor, the potential difference is directly proportional to the current, provided the temperature remains constant.

b Your sketch should have axes labelled V/V and I/A and show a straight line through the origin.

c If the component is ohmic, the graph will be a straight line through the origin.

d If V is plotted against I, the resistance will be equal to the gradient.

53 $\ln(8.2) - \ln(8.0) = 2.10 - 2.08 = 0.02$
$\ln(8.4) - \ln(8.2) = 2.13 - 2.10 = 0.03$
The point $\ln(8.2) = 2.10$ should be plotted with an error bar between 2.08 and 2.13

54 The graph should be a straight line of negative slope. The gradient is equal to $-\lambda$ (where λ is the decay constant).
Then $t_{1/2} = \dfrac{\ln 2}{\lambda} = \dfrac{0.693}{\lambda}$

55 a percentage difference = $\dfrac{(28.3 - 26.7)\,N\,m^{-1}}{27.5\,N\,m^{-1}} \times 100\% = 6\%$

b percentage difference = $\dfrac{(9.81 - 9.71)\,m\,s^{-2}}{9.81\,m\,s^{-2}} \times 100\% = 1\%$

Knowledge check answers

56 a $\ln T = \ln\left(\dfrac{2\pi}{\sqrt{k}}\right) + \dfrac{1}{2}\ln m$

b Gradient $= \dfrac{1}{2} = 0.50$

c Intercept $= \ln\left(\dfrac{2\pi}{\sqrt{k/\mathrm{N\,m^{-1}}}}\right) = 0.19$

$\Rightarrow \dfrac{2\pi}{\sqrt{k/\mathrm{N\,m^{-1}}}} = e^{0.19} = 1.21$

$k = \left(\dfrac{2\pi}{1.21}\right)^2 = 27\,\mathrm{N\,m^{-1}}$

57 Using $s = ut + \frac{1}{2}at^2$
$1.2\,\mathrm{m} = 0 + (\frac{1}{2} \times 9.8\,\mathrm{m\,s^{-2}} \times t^2)$
$t = 0.49\,\mathrm{s} \approx 0.5\,\mathrm{s}$

58 a To ensure that the ball drops vertically in the same position relative to the two light gates.

b Using $v = u + at$, so $a = \dfrac{v - u}{t}$, where a is acceleration due to gravity.

59 $E = \dfrac{Fl}{A\Delta l} \Rightarrow \Delta l = \dfrac{Fl}{AE}$

$\Delta l = \dfrac{5.0\,\mathrm{N} \times 3.0\,\mathrm{m}}{\pi \times \left(0.188 \times 10^{-3}\,\mathrm{m}\right)^2 \times 1.2 \times 10^{11}\,\mathrm{N\,m^{-2}}}$

$= 1.1 \times 10^{-3}\,\mathrm{m} \approx 1\,\mathrm{mm}$

60 a This gives a value for the original length of the wire that is being stretched. You do not need to know how much the wire past the marker stretches.

b This reduces errors due to the production process of the wire in case the wire is not uniform.

61 Stress $= F/A$

$= \dfrac{2.00\,\mathrm{kg} \times 9.8\,\mathrm{N\,kg^{-1}}}{\pi \times \left(0.19 \times 10^{-3}\,\mathrm{m}\right)^2} = 1.73 \times 10^8\,\mathrm{Pa}$

Strain $= \Delta l / l$

$= \dfrac{4.0 \times 10^{-3}\,\mathrm{m}}{2.94\,\mathrm{m}} = 1.36 \times 10^{-3}$

$E = \dfrac{\text{stress}}{\text{strain}} = \dfrac{1.73 \times 10^8\,\mathrm{Pa}}{1.36 \times 10^{-3}} = 1.3 \times 10^{11}\,\mathrm{Pa}$

62 Units for E are $\dfrac{\mathrm{N\,m^{-1} \times m}}{\mathrm{m^2}} = \mathrm{N\,m^{-2}} = \mathrm{Pa}$

63 $R = \dfrac{\rho l}{A} = \dfrac{1.08 \times 10^{-6}\,\Omega\,\mathrm{m} \times 0.50\,\mathrm{m}}{\pi \times \left(\frac{1}{2} \times 0.315 \times 10^{-3}\,\mathrm{m}\right)^2}$

$= 6.93\,\Omega \approx 7\,\Omega$

64 $\rho = \dfrac{1}{\sigma} = \dfrac{1}{58.5 \times 10^6\,\Omega^{-1}\mathrm{m^{-1}}}$

$= 1.71 \times 10^{-8}\,\Omega\,\mathrm{m}$

This is a low resistivity (compared with nichrome, for example), so reduces the resistive losses in the wire.

65 $R = \dfrac{\rho l}{A} \Rightarrow A = \dfrac{\rho l}{R} \Rightarrow \dfrac{\pi d^2}{4} = \dfrac{\rho l}{R}$

$\Rightarrow d = \sqrt{\dfrac{4\rho l}{\pi R}}$

$d = \sqrt{\dfrac{4 \times 1.08 \times 10^{-6}\,\Omega\,\mathrm{m} \times 1.00\,\mathrm{m}}{\pi \times 18.3\,\Omega}}$

$d = 2.74 \times 10^{-4}\,\mathrm{m}$ (or 0.274 mm)

66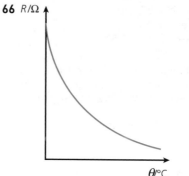

67 $V_{out} = V_{in} \times \dfrac{R_2}{R_1 + R_2}$

$V_{out} = 6.0\,\mathrm{V} \times \dfrac{330\,\Omega}{(330 + 470)\,\Omega} = 2.48\,\mathrm{V}$

$= 2.5\,\mathrm{V}$ within the 2% tolerance

68 Use an LDR and a $100\,\mathrm{k}\Omega$ resistor in series with a power supply. Connect a voltmeter or multimeter across the resistor.

Place a tube over the LDR and fix a lamp above the tube. Reduce the level of light either by placing small squares of tracing paper over the top of the tube or by moving the light further above the tube.

Measure the p.d. across the resistor for different light levels.

69 $n\lambda = d\sin\theta \Rightarrow \sin\theta = \dfrac{n\lambda}{d} = \dfrac{1 \times 550 \times 10^{-9}\,\mathrm{m}}{\left(300 \times 10^3\,\mathrm{m^{-1}}\right)^{-1}} = 0.165$

$\theta = \sin^{-1}(0.165) = 9.5° \approx 10°$

70 a The distances would be greater (as the wavelength is longer).

b $n = \dfrac{d\sin\theta}{\lambda}$ and $\sin\theta \leq 1$

$n \leq \dfrac{\left(300 \times 10^3\,\mathrm{m^{-1}}\right)^{-1} \times 1}{693 \times 10^{-9}\,\mathrm{m}} \leq 4.8$

n must be an integer, so $n_{max} = 4$

71 a The waves emitted from the two slits originate from the same wavefront. As all the points on a wavefront are in phase, the waves emitted by the slits must be coherent.

b From $x = \dfrac{\lambda D}{a} \Rightarrow \lambda = \dfrac{ax}{D}$

$\lambda = \dfrac{1.0 \times 10^{-3}\,\text{m} \times 0.50 \times 10^{-3}\,\text{m}}{0.80\,\text{m}}$

$\lambda = 6.25 \times 10^{-7}\,\text{m} = 625\,\text{nm}$

72 $E = hf$

$E = 6.63 \times 10^{-34}\,\text{J s} \times 5.60 \times 10^{13}\,\text{Hz}$

$E = 3.71 \times 10^{-20}\,\text{J} \approx 4 \times 10^{-20}\,\text{J}$

73 Energy gained $= eV$

$= 1.6 \times 10^{-19}\,\text{C} \times 2.5\,\text{V} = 4.0 \times 10^{-19}\,\text{J}$

74 From $A = A_0 e^{-\mu x}$, a graph of A against x is an exponential curve, starting at $A = A_0$ with a downward concave curve that *does not meet the x-axis*. The axes should be labelled A and x.

75 Your graph should have axes labelled A/min^{-1} and x/mm, with a *smooth* exponential curve of best fit. The half-thickness can be read off for $A = 202.5\,\text{min}^{-1}$, giving a value for $x_{\frac{1}{2}}$ of about 11.6 mm. The activity will fall to a quarter of its initial value in *two* half-thicknesses, i.e. 23.2 mm. This shows that the graph is exponential.

76 If p remains constant, then $V \propto T$.
If V doubles, then T must double.
$T_1 = 294\,\text{K}$, so doubling gives $T_2 = 588\,\text{K}$ or 315°C.

77 To show direct proportionality, your graph should be a straight line through the origin.

78 a $t = RC$

$t = 3.4 \times 10^3\,\Omega \times 220 \times 10^{-6}\,\text{F} = 0.75\,\text{s} \sim 1\,\text{s}$

b In $V = V_0 e^{-t/RC}$, t/RC must be just a number, without any unit. Thus RC must have the same unit as t, i.e. second.

c $R = \dfrac{V}{I}$ and $C = \dfrac{Q}{V}$, so

$CR = \dfrac{V}{I} \times \dfrac{Q}{V} = \dfrac{Q}{I} = \dfrac{C}{C\,\text{s}^{-1}} = \text{s}$

79 $I = V/R$

$= 6.0\,\text{V}/(3.34 \times 10^3\,\Omega) = 1.8\,\text{mA}$

80 Squaring $T = 2\pi\sqrt{\dfrac{l}{g}}$ on both sides gives:

$T^2 = 4\pi^2\,\dfrac{l}{g} = \dfrac{4\pi^2}{g} \times l$

81 This will allow the pendulum to settle down with steady simple harmonic motion. If the pendulum is not released smoothly, it may oscillate erratically for the first one or two oscillations.

82 From $F = kx \Rightarrow k = F/x$

$k = \dfrac{0.300\,\text{kg} \times 9.81\,\text{m s}^{-2}}{0.110\,\text{m}}$

$k = 26.8\,\text{kg s}^{-2}\,(\text{N m}^{-1})$

Using $T = 2\pi\sqrt{\dfrac{m}{k}}$, squaring and rearranging gives:

$k = \dfrac{4\pi^2}{T^2}\,m = \dfrac{4\pi^2}{0.670^2\,\text{s}^2} \times 0.300\,\text{kg}$

$k = 26.4\,\text{kg s}^{-2}\,(\text{N m}^{-1})$

83 Using $\Delta E = mc\Delta\theta \Rightarrow \Delta\theta = \dfrac{\Delta E}{mc} = \dfrac{P\Delta t}{mc}$

since $\Delta E = P\Delta t$ for the kettle. So:

$\Delta\theta = \dfrac{2000\,\text{W} \times 60\,\text{s}}{0.800\,\text{kg} \times 4200\,\text{J kg}^{-1}\,\text{K}^{-1}} = 35.7\,\text{K}$

Therefore final temperature $= (20 + 35.7)°\text{C} \approx 56°\text{C}$

84 Energy lost by hot water ΔE_h = energy gained by cold water ΔE_c.
Let θ = final temperature, then:
$\Delta E_h = m_h c(55 - \theta)$ and $\Delta E_c = m_c c(\theta - 10)$
$\Rightarrow m_h c(55 - \theta) = m_c c(\theta - 10)$
Dividing both sides by c and kg:
$0.4(55 - \theta) = 0.2(\theta - 10)$
$22 - 0.4\theta = 0.2\theta - 2$

giving $\theta = \dfrac{24}{0.60} = 40°\text{C}$

The water will be lukewarm (just).

85 If energy is transferred to the surroundings, not all the energy from the block will be transferred to the water. So, the final steady temperature will be lower than it should be, which will give a value for the specific heat capacity of the block that is too *small*.

Index

Index